COLUMBIA HOUSE

# the world of automobiles

## An Illustrated Encyclopedia of the Motor Car

COLUMBIA HOUSE/New York

**Consultant Editor:** Tom Northey
**Executive Editor:** Ian Ward
**Editorial Director:** Brian Innes
**Assistant Editors:** Laurie Caddell
Mike Winfield
**Art Editor:** David Goodman

**Contributors**
ENRICA ACETI: Autobianchi
PAUL DAVIES: Autocross
L. J. K. SETRIGHT: Automatic
transmission
Axle
JOHN BOLSTER: Auto Union
DAVID BURGESS WISE: Barnato
Bean
BRIAN INNES: Baker
TONY OSMAN: Battery
L. J. K. SETRIGHT: Balancing
Bearings
MIKE TWITE: Bandini
Behra
IAN WARD: Bad-weather driving
NICK BRITTAN: Beltoise
DAVID BURGESS WISE: Bentley
JERRY SLONIGER: Benz
ALFRED WOOLF: Bertone
DAVID BURGESS WISE: Bira
Birkin
Bluebird
ALFRED WOOLF: Bianchi
JERRY SLONIGER: BMW

DAVID BURGESS WISE: Bollée
Bordino
TOM NORTHEY: Bodywork repairs
L. J. K. SETRIGHT: Brabham cars
MIKE TWITE: Bonnier
Borgward
Brabham, Jack
HARRY LOFTUS: Breakdown
GRAHAM MACBETH:
Brands Hatch
British Grand Prix

MIKE TWITE: Breedlove
L. J. K. SETRIGHT:
Brakes and braking
Bristol

# Contents                                                                Page

## Austin Allegro

The Allegro was the 1973 addition to the Austin range, being offered in four engine sizes: 1100 cc, 1300 cc, 1500 cc and 1750 cc. All these are mounted transversely at the front and all of them drive the front wheels.

The 1100 and 1300 engines are the old faithful 'A' Series units used in the Minis and 1100 derivatives, while the others are borrowed from the Maxi. Power outputs range from 47 bhp for the 1100 to 80 bhp for the 1750.

Gearboxes, which are mounted under the engines, are four-speed on the 1100 and 1300s and five-speed on the Maxi-engined models. Synchromesh is fitted to all forward gears.

Final drive is mounted behind the engine in all cases, but is by hypoid bevel or helical spur gears, depending on the engine.

The suspension is the most publicised feature of the Allegro range. It is known as Hydragas and uses gas springs with fluid damping and interconnection. At the front, the Hydragas displacers are linked with unequal length transverse arms, while the rear units are supported by trailing arms. Damping is integral with the Hydragas system.

All seven Allegro models share the same brakes, having discs at the front and drums behind. The top four cars—1500s and 1750s—are fitted with a vacuum servo as standard, while this item is offered as an extra with the others. The handbrake operates the rear brake shoes by means of cables.

Rack-and-pinion steering is used, mounted behind the front wheels for safety. The Allegro's steering included the only visible unusual point about the range—the 'Quartic' steering wheel, which was simply a squared-off normal type.

Two and four-door bodies are available, all having four seats. On some models reclining front seats are a standard fitting. Monocoque construction is utilised for the body/chassis.

ENGINE: Front-mounted, transverse, in-line 4, water cooled. 65 mm bore × 84 mm stroke = 1098 cc or 71 mm bore × 81 mm stroke = 1275 cc or 76 mm bore × 81 mm stroke = 1485 cc or 76 mm bore × 96 mm stroke = 1748 cc. Maximum power 47 bhp (DIN) at 5250 rpm (1100), 57 bhp (DIN) at 5300 rpm (1300), 72 bhp (DIN) at 5500 rpm (1500), 80 bhp at 5000 rpm (1750); maximum torque 60 lb ft (DIN) at 2450 rpm (1100), 69 lb ft (DIN) at 3000 rpm (1300), 80 lb ft at 3250 rpm (1500), 100 lb ft at 2600 rpm (1750); maximum engine rpm 6500. Cast-iron cylinder block and head; compression ratio 8.5:1 (1100), 8.8:1 (1300), 9:1 (1500), 8.8:1 (1750); 3 main bearings (1100 and 1300) 5 main bearings (1500 and 1750). 2 valves per cylinder operated by 1 block-mounted camshaft via pushrods and rockers (1100 and 1300) or by 1 overhead camshaft. 1 SU sidedraught carburettor.

TRANSMISSION: Single-plate clutch; 4-speed, all-synchromesh gearbox (1100 and 1300—ratios 1st 3.53, 2nd 2.2, 3rd 1.43, 4th 1, reverse 3.54:1) or 5-speed, all-synchromesh gearbox (1500 and 1750—ratios 1st 3.41, 2nd 2.13, 3rd 1.46, 4th 1.07, 5th 0.93, reverse 3.47:1); helical spur gear final drive (ratio 4.13:1—1100, 3.94:1—1300, 3.65:1—1500/1750) driving front wheels.

CHASSIS: Monocoque unit.

SUSPENSION: Front—independent by transverse unequal-length arms and Hydragas units; rear—independent by trailing arms and Hydragas units.

STEERING: Rack-and-pinion; 3.6 turns from lock to lock.

BRAKES: Hydraulic discs front and drums rear, with servo assistance standard on 1500 and 1750; total swept area 254 sq in; handbrake operating on rear wheels.

WHEELS: 4½ in × 13 pressed steel.

TYRES: 145SR × 13 or 155SR × 13 (1750).

DIMENSIONS AND WEIGHT: Wheelbase 96.25 in; track 53.5 in front, 53.6 in rear; length 151.75 in; width 63.5 in; height 55 in; ground clearance 72.25 in; kerb weight 1815–2011 lb; turning circle between walls 35.5 ft; fuel tank 10.5 gals.

BODY: Saloon; 2 or 4 doors; 4 seats (reclining front seats available).

PERFORMANCE: Maximum speed —1100 81.4 mph, 1300 82 mph, 1500 93.7 mph, 1750SS 95.6 mph; 0–60 mph—1100 19.9 secs, 1300 18.4 secs, 1500 14.2 secs, 1750SS 12.7 secs; standing ¼-mile—1100 21.2 secs, 1300 20.9 secs, 1500 19.6 secs, 1750SS 18.9 secs; fuel consumption—1100 30.6 mpg, 1300 35 mpg, 1500 34.7 mpg, 1750SS 22.8 mpg.

# The Austin 2200

Utilising the well proven 1800 body shell, the Austin 2200 was introduced to replace the unfortunate 3-litre. The engine is a stretched version of the overhead-cam Maxi unit, now sporting six cylinders instead of four, but still mounted transversely in the engine bay and driving the front wheels.

To fit the longer (wider) engine under the bonnet, the radiator has been moved to the front and air circulation is taken care of by a thermostatically controlled electric fan.

The six cylinders give the engine a capacity of 2227 cc and a power output of 110 bhp. Torque produced is 126 lb ft and the top speed resulting from these figures is 103 mph.

The gearbox is mounted underneath the engine and has four forward speeds, all with synchromesh. The change is linked by an unusual hydraulic arrangement. From the gearbox, the power flow is taken back-

wards to the helical spur gear final drive, in line with the front wheels which it drives.

Suspension is looked after by Hydrolastic displacers, double wishbones and lower trailing links at the front, while at the rear the Hydrolastic displacers are accompanied by trailing arms, which are mounted firmly enough to support all the suspension loads.

Rack-and-pinion steering is fitted and power-assistance is available as an optional extra.

Front discs and rear drums are hydraulically operated with servo assistance, to make sure that the brake pedal pressures are not too high. The handbrake is cable operated and controls the rear drums.

The four-door saloon body is of monocoque construction and houses four to five seats. Reclining backrests are an option for the front seats.

ENGINE: Front-mounted, in-line 6, water cooled. 76.1 mm (3 in) bore × 83.7 mm (3.3 in) stroke

= 2227 cc (135.9 cu in). Maximum power (DIN) 110 bhp at 5250 rpm; maximum torque (DIN) 126 lb ft at 3500 rpm; maximum engine rpm 6000. Cast-iron block and head with aluminium gearbox and final-drive casings in unit; compression ratio 9:1; 4 main bearings. 2 valves per cylinder operated by 1 chain-driven overhead camshaft. 2 SU sidedraught carburettors.

TRANSMISSION: Single-plate clutch; 4-speed, all-synchromesh gearbox (ratios 1st 3.292, 2nd 2.059, 3rd 1.384, 4th 1, reverse 3.075:1); helical spur gear final drive (ratio 3.882:1) driving front wheels.

CHASSIS: Monocoque body/chassis.

SUSPENSION: Front—independent by double wishbones, lower trailing links and Hydrolastic displacers; rear—independent by trailing arms and Hydrolastic displacers.

STEERING: Rack-and-pinion; 3.56 turns from lock to lock.

BRAKES: Servo-assisted, hydraulically operated discs front and drums rear; total swept area 294 sq in; handbrake operating on rear wheels.

WHEELS: $4\frac{1}{2}$ in J × 14 pressed steel.

TYRES: 165 × 14

DIMENSIONS AND WEIGHT: Wheelbase 105.87 in; track 55.91 in front, 55.47 in rear; length 166.18 in; width 66.93 in; height 56.14 in; ground clearance 6.5 in; kerb weight 2511 lb; turning circle between walls 40.3 ft; fuel tank 10.5 gals.

BODY: Saloon; 4 doors; 4/5 seats.

PERFORMANCE: Speeds in the gears—1st 35 mph, 2nd 55 mph, 3rd 80 mph, 4th 104 mph; acceleration—0–60 mph 13.1 secs, standing $\frac{1}{4}$-mile 18.7 secs; fuel consumption 28 mpg.

# SIMPLY A FIAT WITH A DIFFERENCE

The Autobianchi Primula introduced in 1964 used an 1100 cc Fiat engine mounted transversely and powering the front wheels. It was a typical example of Fiat using Autobianchi as a proving ground for ideas to be further developed in future years

ALTHOUGH the name of the Italian concern derives from the long-established Fabbrica Automobili Velocipedi Edoardo Bianchi & Co, Autobianchi has no direct connection with its predecessor.

The firm of Edoardo Bianchi was founded in 1885, in the first place to manufacture bicycles; like many other cycle manufacturers, it soon graduated to cars, and the name of Bianchi was well-known in Italy in the years between 1905 and 1939. After the war, however, the company found great difficulty in getting back into car manufacture, and in 1954 the engineer Ferruccio Quintavelle succeeded in interesting Fiat and Pirelli in the production potential of the factory at Desio, and in the prestige of the company's name. In January 1955 a new company was formed, Bianchi, Fiat and Pirelli each holding one third. In September 1956 the rundown of Bianchi's Desio factory began, but it was not until June 1958 that Autobianchi formally acquired the premises. This period saw the final financial crises of Bianchi, the dismissal of Guiseppe Bianchi as managing director of Autobianchi, and the division of the shares of the company between the two surviving partners.

It is easy to understand Pirelli's reasons for the investment: they had found a new outlet for their tyres. Fiat's reasons are not so clear. Their aim seemed to be to produce an extension of their own car range, designed for people 'who want to be noticed'. They also wanted to produce models with, at that time, such experimental features as front-wheel drive, without being bound by their trademark.

The Fiat 500-based car, known as the Bianchina, was unveiled in September 1957, but distribution did not begin until the early months of 1958. In true Bianchi tradition, the new car employed conventional techniques in a model offering greater distinction and comfort than the low-priced Fiat version from which it derived its major components and inspiration. In the Bianchina's first year of production, 11,000 cars were manufactured at the Desio plant. The model's success was indisputable and this fact led to the announcement of a new range, based on the original model: the Bianchina Special came on the scene, as did the four-door normal and special, the Panoramica, the Cabriolet and the small-van version.

In 1964, an engineer called Giovanni Nasi took over the chairmanship of the company, showing the first sign of the complete Fiat takeover which was approaching. In the autumn of that year, the Primula appeared. Again, this employed standard Fiat components, in

this case derived from the Fiat 1100, and used in a distinctive way. The Primula, with its transverse engine and front-wheel drive, served two purposes. It introduced a mechanical formula with which the Italians were still unfamiliar and it provided the Fiat organisation with a practical proving ground for ideas which were to be much further developed in the years ahead.

The Pirelli group withdrew from the company in 1968 and Autobianchi was merged with Fiat while continuing to retain its autonomy and its own independent production line. The following year, the Desio factory was enlarged and production of the Fiat 500L was added to the range.

In 1970, two new Autobianchi models were introduced. One was the A111, a small, de-luxe, four-door development of the Primula, offering to the public a more expensive, better equipped and more powerful alternative to the Fiat 128, from which it was evolved. The other was the A112, a delightful, quality small car with a 903 cc engine producing 47 bhp. This proved to be the forerunner of the 127, which emerged in the Fiat range a year later. The elegant A112 achieved a

The Fiat 500-based Bianchina was the first Autobianchi, unveiled in 1957, and it proved to be one of the company's most popular models, with over 11,000 cars being built in the first year of production. It utilised the twin-cylinder, 497 cc, air-cooled Fiat engine

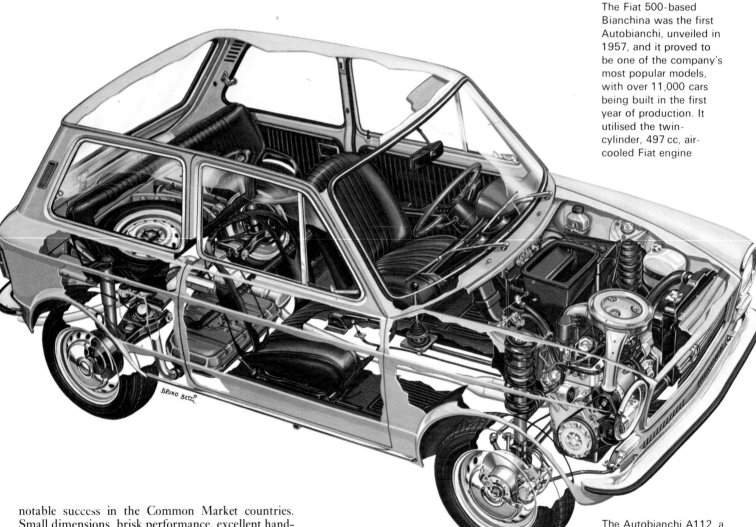

notable success in the Common Market countries. Small dimensions, brisk performance, excellent handling characteristics and good quality finish and equipment gave it a place in the market for which there is little competition. Such was the demand for the A112 that, in 1972, production of the A111 ceased so that the additional capacity could be made available for the A112 which, in 1973, was produced in three versions, taking up more than 50 per cent of the daily output from the Desio factory.

Autobianchi is now very much an integrated part of the Fiat empire, although the company still retains its own identity, even to the point of Fiat adopting the Autobianchi trademark for some of their smaller models, now produced at Desio.          EA

The Autobianchi A112, a delightful, quality small car, with a 903 cc, four-cylinder engine producing 47 bhp. This now takes up more than 50% of the daily output from the Autobianchi factory

# KEEPING ON THE GRASS

High-speed thrills and spills are the order of the day when the autocross circus takes to the dirt. What began as fun for the family man is now serious business

'Mr Autocross' John Bevan, who, with his Naveb Special, powered by a tuned Lotus twin-cam engine, has dominated the sport for the past four years

Two of the most popular family saloons racing are the Hillman Imp (top) and the ubiquitous Mini (bottom)

NOWHERE is motor sport stronger from the competitor's point of view than in the British Isles. Of the many varied branches of the sport not one could be more British—although it is now beginning to spread to other countries—than autocross. Sporting enthusiasts traditionally divide themselves into two very basic factions in Britain: the rough surface people and the tarmac racers. The most popular single sport for the motor enthusiast is rallying, and as much of this is essentially slippery or loose surface driving it is no surprise that autocross has spawned many of the current leading British rally drivers.

Autocross is the very essence of motor club participation. The sport first began to formulate its pattern in the mid 1950s and has progressed to such a point that during 1973 over 270 meetings were held throughout the UK and there are now two national championships.

The object is quite simple. The course, between half and one mile in length, is set out on what is usually called 'smooth' grassland. To the autocross participant it is smooth—to the family motorist rough. The track will be fairly tight with a number of sharp bends and usually a fast straight that allows more powerful cars to reach speeds approaching 100 mph. In most cases the course is wide enough to allow two cars to race side by side (and sufficient to allow these cars to travel sideways as often happens) and the start area will be a slip road connected to the track itself.

Normally two cars will start at once and complete two or three laps of the circuit. Although the two cars are in fact racing against each other, the prime object is to record a faster total time for the laps than your opponent or anyone else in your class. The very nature of the track means that whoever gets ahead from the start line is likely to stay ahead, unless he spins off the course or hits one of the many flags which act as corner markers. Hitting flags—driving off the planned track—means that penalties are imposed. Roughly half a lap after the start of one pair of cars, another two are started, giving spectators the chance to see four cars on the track at once.

Cars are, of course, divided into classes and drivers compete to lead their class at the end of the day's racing.

They also compete to achieve the elusive fastest time of the day (often known as FTD, or B—best—TD).

A typical event will last a complete day and allow all the 100 or so competitors two practice sessions during the morning and two or three timed runs during the afternoon. It's the fastest time for one of these runs that counts in the final results. Further interest is often added by the formation of three-car teams from different classes scoring on aggregate and, on occasions, racing may end with a knock-out contest between the over-all fastest cars at the event, irrespective of classes.

In a few places cars are started four at a time for autocross meetings but this is only permissible when the Royal Automobile Club, which sanctions motor sport events in Britain, has agreed that a particular track is wide enough and that existing protection facilities for spectators are adequate. Neither of the two British championship events—the RAC National Autocross Championship or the Castrol/British Trials & Rally Drivers' Association Clubman's Championship—runs four-car races.

Autocross is essentially a sport for the motor club. Initially it was developed for the average man to take his average car along to the event, throw out the wife, kids and baggage, tape over the headlights, chalk his competition number on the doors and then go racing. However—as in all sports, not only motoring—the whole concept has grown to a very professional level, although it is still mainly the domain of the amateur and a season's autocrossing can be relatively inexpensive compared with other forms of motor sport.

Initially, drivers decided that the cars they were using were not fast enough. Standard engines and suspension systems became highly modified and, as engine power increased, the need for specially treaded 'chunky' tyres became obvious. Weight was reduced by replacing heavy steel boot, bonnet and door panels with light, flexible, glassfibre replicas, and strong roll-over cages were added to prevent injury during the rolls that became more frequent as speeds increased.

The final blow to the original concept of autocross came when competitors realised that their highly developed cars were not suitable to be driven on the road, and anyway how were they going to get home if the car broke? By the 1969 national final all cars were on trailers—except one, the TVR sports car of Ron Easton who deserves special mention for this feat! But despite the advance of technology, autocross is still for the amateur. One big reason for this is that it has never been a spectator sport, but primarily one for the competitor, mechanic and friends. Prize money is almost non existent and the only incentive to the competitor is to beat old rivals and to enjoy himself.

The class structure for events is simple and in the main follows the natural splitting of makes or types of car into competitive groups. Front-wheel-drive classes are split at the 850 cc and 1000 cc points to allow the three basic types of British Leyland Mini (the 848 cc saloon, the 1000 Cooper and the 1275S) to run against their own kind. Rear-wheel-drive cars with rear engines have a class all their own, which puts tiny Hillman Imps running against big bore Volkswagens but, surprisingly, they are comparative. Generally 'conventional' front-engined, rear-drive cars are split at the 1300 cc mark. In fact these last two classes have seen, in recent years, an almost complete domination by the 1300 and 1600 versions of the Ford Escort cars run as one class—there used to be two but poor entries in this section have meant amalgamation. Finally, there are the specials.

Potentially the autocross special must be the fastest car. Built specifically for the task, it is light in weight, but with maximum possible power and controllability. Designs differ considerably in this class but emerging as unbeatable is the mid-engine spaceframe format. Proof of this must be the fact that for the past four years the National Autocross Champion has been the driver of such a car: in fact the same driver, garage owner John Bevan, and the same car, the Naveb (Bevan backwards).

John Bevan built his Championship winning car himself on an initial outlay of under £300. To design the chassis, John sat on the floor of his garage and friends marked out the areas for engine and gearbox behind him, then drew chalk lines around the reclining Bevan and essential mechanicals. When it was finished the chalk marks left were designated the parameters for the car and chassis construction from welded square tubing began.

Power unit for the car was a modified Lotus-Ford twin-cam engine of 1600 cc, giving around 160 bhp, and the gearbox was taken from a Volkswagen Transporter and turned upside down to allow for the fact that the transmission normally sits in front, not behind, the engine. The suspension for the Championship-winning special utilised Morris Minor torsion bars at the rear and Triumph Herald springs and axles at the front.

In this car Bevan has been supreme. The design of the vehicle has helped considerably, but the lack of success of other cars copying the Naveb lines, some with more powerful engines, has shown that much of the secret lies in the skill of the quiet spoken man from the West Country.

As the most successful autocross competitor in Britain, Bevan won a total of around £200 for his 1972 season's racing; his sponsorship deals with a motor magazine, oil company and tyre manufacturer probably totalled no more than an additional £200. The price of fame is low in autocross!

Bevan runs in a class that, although the fastest, is not the most keenly contested. In some other classes a winning car can be a lot more expensive than John Bevan's. Peter Harrold's 1972 Championship class-winning Volkswagen used a 2.2-litre engine 'stretched' by using a special crankshaft, the 1300 Minis of such drivers as Terry Smith (who is the 1973 BT & RDA

Champion) and Nick Jesty use full race-tune engines and such sophistications as lightweight trailer suspension at the rear. In the big saloon class an Escort to beat front runners George Warren and Ron Douglas could cost over £4000 if purchased as a new car.

Driving in an autocross event requires special skills and tactics. The weather can play a big part in the results—slippery grass or mud will favour the lower powered cars with weight over the driven wheels, while a bone-dry track needs every possible horse power. Conditions may change completely during a day's racing: a wet track for practice can dry out and completely reverse recorded times from earlier sessions while a soft course will cut up badly during the day and final runs will not only be slower but more hazardous, as deep ruts can easily flip a fast travelling car if they are hit at the wrong angle.

Getting ahead at the start is a vital part of the battle. Autocross driving, like rallying, is not so much a

*Below:* contrast in autocross styles: the popular Volkswagen that runs in the rear-engined, rear-drive class and the front-engined Triumph Spitfire

matter of controlling the car but maintaining a certain lack of control. Cars are deliberately thrown sideways for corners, either to scrub off speed in a situation where braking would simply cause the car to travel straight on at the bend, or to set the car up correctly for the fastest possible exit from the bend. A surplus of power is needed to execute such manoeuvres but indiscriminate use of this is likely to land the driver in trouble. A very real problem for the man who does end up second is that of dust on a dry track. Sometimes this can be so bad the driver just cannot see where he is going.

Accidents are often spectacular but injuries extremely rare. Deliberate baulking or 'nerfing' another competitor is not allowed although cars do sometimes touch in tight bends and the most common upset is a roll which usually wrecks the car but not the driver. Marshals, firefighting equipment and medical facilities are required and often are as good as those at a track meeting. Spectator protection is not as strict because autocross, with only four cars on the track at the same time, is classed in Britain as a speed event, not a race.

Autocross in Britain continues to advance. In recent years attempts have been made to introduce a class for standard production cars in an effort to cut costs and allow cars to be driven to the event. This is failing at present because the only competitive 'standard' car is a nearly new one that has been fitted with all the possible and legal performance options listed by the manufacturer. Tighter control of this class may see it thriving in the future.

The sport is spreading. On the Continent, Dutch and German enthusiasts have taken up autocross and in the USA events of a roughly similar nature are run under the name of gymkhanas—a name that means something totally different in Britain. PD

*Above:* autocross drivers not only compete against each other and the clock, but also against the difficult and often treacherous terrain. A TVR and a modified Ford Anglia are shown in action

# TAKING THE EFFORT OUT OF DRIVING

As ever-increasing traffic reduces driving to a grind, the effortless ease of the automatic gearbox is becoming more popular and more commonly available

The 'automatic' automatic. The DAF Variomatic transmission utilises a belt-and-pulley system which provides a steplessly variable change between the highest and lowest ratios available

ACCORDING to the degree of automaticity offered, an automatic transmission is one that relieves the driver of the skills and obligations of gear changing and/or clutch operation. Ideally it will ensure that for any given combination of vehicle speed and engine load it will automatically provide a suitable gear ratio for the transmission and multiplication of engine torque to the driving wheels. This ideal is seldom achieved, though efforts have been made since the earliest day of the motor car. Spaulding in 1897, Fouillaron in 1900, and several later designers and manufacturers, conceived a steplessly-variable-ratio belt transmission, while in the 1930s the epicyclic gearbox enjoyed some limited popularity either in the Wilson form as a pre-selective mechanism combined with a fluid coupling, or as a Cotal gearbox in which gears were electro-magnetically held under the control of a simple electric switch. Nevertheless, the simple friction clutch and manually operated gearbox, perfectly summarised by the pioneer Panhard with the words *C'est brutal, mais ça marche*, has in successively refined forms held sway from the dawn of motoring to the present day, being still pre-dominant in all major countries outside the USA.

It is not to be supposed that four generations of designers have all had the same blind spot. In retaining the old cogbox so long they have been justified by its reasonable reliability and high efficiency. At least it is high in mechanical efficiency, absorbing and wasting very little of the precious power it is meant to transmit: but as an agent of transmission it is by no means efficient overall.

The trouble is that the variation of transmission ratio in such a gearbox can only be made in a limited series of finite steps, each constituting a fixed gear ratio and therefore inconsistent with the characteristic power delivery of a piston engine. In each gear there is only one road speed at which the engine can deliver full effort, so that with a five-speed box there are only five speeds at which the car can be getting the utmost from its power unit. The rest of the time the engine will be struggling up through its working range or wheezing away beyond it; and although the cogs may faithfully transmit, say, 96% of the effort to final drive, it will still be only 96% of something that may be a lot less than maximum torque. This is why the mechanical efficiency argument is somewhat specious. To put it in

## Automatic transmission

simple terms, 86% of maximum effort all the time may be better than 96% occasionally.

Once people accept this idea they are well on the way to accepting the idea of automatic transmissions. Ultimately we can look forward to a transmission offering stepless variation of gear ratio from as low as may be needed to as high as could be managed in the most favourable conditions.

Hydrostatics, which can provide this, are on their way but at present are severely limited by problems of noise, vibration, and mechanical inefficiency. Variable belt and pulley drives can also do it and are on the market already. In Germany ZF and Reimers do a steplessly variable belt drive for buses and the like, but the belt squeezed between hydraulically powered pulleys is really a sort of steel chain and 65 bhp is the most that it can be called upon to transmit.

Better known and proving increasingly successful is the DAF Variomatic transmission, which handles the same power in production cars and has dealt with more than 200 bhp in competition cars. It relies upon a set of flexible belts squeezed between the faces of adjustable pulleys that are expanded or contracted automatically so as to provide the most appropriate transmission ratio for prevailing conditions. A system of spring loading and a centrifugally operated servo mechanism ensure that the ratio automatically selected is appropriate to the speed, while a pneumatic mechanism, energised by engine inlet manifold depression, provides for matching the gear ratio to the load.

Full throttle cancels this vacuum secondary control of ratio and ensures maximum possible acceleration by keeping the engine at peak output and letting the car catch up with it; so long as the throttle pedal is kicked right down the transmission will continually adjust the ratio so as to give the highest possible road speed. Releasing the accelerator pedal just a fraction allows vacuum control to be resumed, giving a change up to what may very well be an overdrive ratio.

The supplementary virtue of the Variomatic is that there is no need for the designer to compromise the final drive ratio in order to achieve the best performance: he just picks one that is sure to be somewhat too high, and leaves the pulleys to choose whatever lower overall ratio is appropriate to prevailing circumstances. It is this feature which explains the ability of DAF cars to reach unexpectedly high speeds in favourable conditions (for example, down steep hills) despite their modest power and correspondingly modest true maximum speed in neutral conditions.

However, although the highest Variomatic ratio can be really long-striding, the lowest cannot conveniently be much lower than 4:1. Simple mechanical considerations dictate this, rather than any basic conceptual limitation; but the effect is that the ratios, while being steplessly variable, are not truly infinitely variable. This applies to all automatic transmissions, and necessarily so. If it were otherwise there is not a halfshaft in existence that would not be snapped by the infinitely multiplied torque of the bottom ratio.

In practice, the lowest ratio of an automatic transmission is chosen to give the car as much hillclimbing ability as customers are likely to need. The result is invariably low enough to produce another limiting feature: the coupling between engine and gearbox, whether of the fluid type as in most automatic transmissions or a centrifugal friction clutch as in the DAF (where it is not a necessary part of the Variomatic drive but is included so as to eliminate the clutch pedal and the skills needed to operate it) makes it difficult to get the car off the mark with as much verve as might be expected. Certainly it is seldom that an automatic

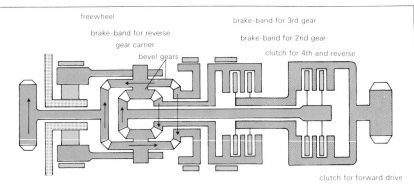

Neutral: all brake-bands and clutches are free; the output shaft is stationary while the rest are idling

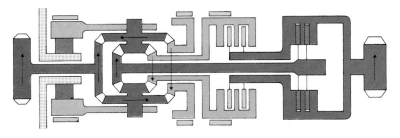

First gear: the gear carrier is fixed and held by the freewheel, the forward clutch is engaged, brake-bands are free

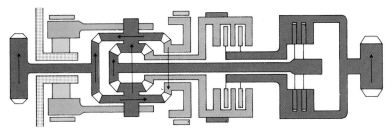

Second gear: the forward clutch is engaged and the second-gear brake-band is fixed

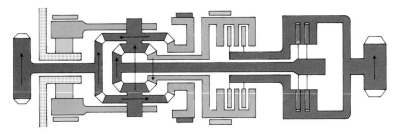

Third gear: the forward clutch is engaged and the third-gear brake-band is fixed

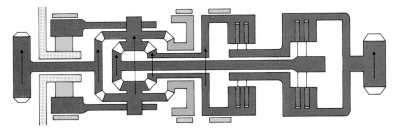

Top gear: both clutches are engaged, so all components are turning in the same direction, at the same speed, giving a ratio of 1:1

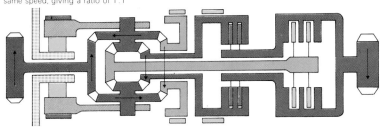

Reverse: the reverse clutch is engaged, and the forward clutch disengaged, while the reverse brake-band is fixed

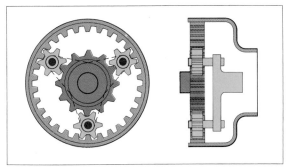

transmission will produce wheelspin in normal driving away from stand-still. In the case of the DAF such initial sluggishness can be offset against surprisingly good acceleration once the car is on the move with the clutch fully engaged and the engine into its stride, when the transmission efficiency never drops below 90% and at mid-range may climb to 94%.

Given a low enough gear ratio, anything can spin its wheels from standstill. Indeed, with high-powered engines it is the limit of tyre adhesion and hence the on-set of uncontrollable wheelspin, rather than the demands of gradients, that determine the starting gear ratio. When the 1937 Grand Prix Auto Union set a world record for the standing kilometre in 18.4 seconds, it was limited by wheelspin in 1st and 2nd gears up to about 100 mph; calculations at the time showed that steplessly variable gearing would only have improved the figure to 18.31 seconds.

Electrical transmissions, which might be supposed the best, can make maximum torque available at all times and provide a quite inimitable degree of control. Electrically driven rail cars can spin their wheels and check the spin again in less than a revolution, but suitable systems have yet to be devised for cars.

At present the most common kind of automatic transmission comprises a constant-mesh planetary or epicyclic gearbox connected to the engine by some kind of hydrokinetic coupling. It usually permits power-sustained or 'hot' shifts—transitions from one gear ratio to the next are in any case very much quicker than any combination of conventional clutch pedal and hand lever can match—and it commonly allows the engine to work at its best speed when under load. The gear-change itself is most commonly worked by oil pressure from a special pump. The pressure operates braking bands and plate-type clutches in order to alter the ratios of epicyclic or bevel gear sets. For a three-speed gearbox, there will usually be two sets, top gear being obtained by locking the input and output shafts together, by means of a plate clutch.

Usually, the change points are governed by engine speed and throttle opening, although a manual over-ride is fitted in most cases. Throttle opening will only have an effect up to certain speeds, where the engine speed will over-rule this. Such a transmission is usually bulky and heavy, it is usually consumptive of power, it often makes towing or push starting impossible, and it

can only be made economically by being manufactured in large numbers. The result of this last and most important detraction is that car manufacturers can seldom buy an automatic precisely suited to their needs and they are not always prepared to match their engines to the transmissions.

Part of the difficulty usually encountered in marrying some ill-suited engine and transmission is the difficulty of ensuring that gear changes take place smoothly, and at exactly the right time, automatically. The timing could just as well be left to the driver, who has in his head a far better and cheaper computer than any of the manufacturers could provide, and might be prepared to move a lever or press a button. The transmission engineers would then be left with the need to devise some way of compensating for a generally rather haphazard treatment of the accelerator pedal by drivers relying on automatic transmissions.

Yet changes can go through with perfect timing and with perfect smoothness, and when the transmission is perfectly matched to the engine the resultant performance can be of a high standard. This can only be achieved when torque converter characteristics, gear ratios and engine performance are all properly reconciled. There is a limit to what can be achieved in the way of choosing gear ratios when using conventional epicyclic gear trains (or their bevel-differential equivalents as found in the Automotive Products gearbox), but the limitations are not onerous in practice. That leaves the engines and the converter to be matched, and this is a business whose subtlety can only be appreciated after some study of the whole range of hydrokinetic couplings of which there are many different kinds.

Of those that are most familiar to motorists, there

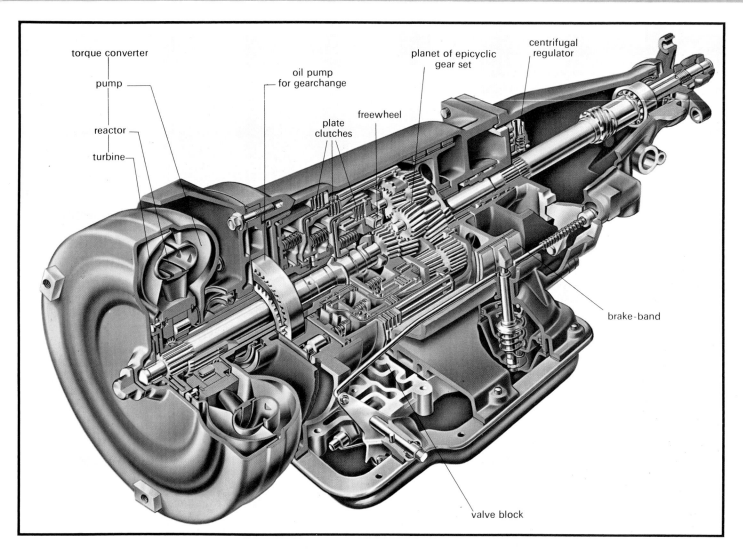

torque converter

pump

reactor

turbine

oil pump
for gearchange

plate
clutches

freewheel

planet of epicyclic
gear set

centrifugal
regulator

brake-band

valve block

A cutaway view of the General Motors Hydramatic transmission, detailing the components. There have been many versions of this gearbox, some with more than one torque converter, some with a lock-up clutch to override the torque converter in top gear

is some difference between the torque converter and the simple fluid flywheel. The latter is much the less complex, and since it is still used in some Mercedes–Benz cars it gives us a suitable starting point.

To be strict we should call it a fluid coupling. It is simple in construction, comprising two radially vaned saucers face to face. Oil flung centrifugally by one is caught by the other, the force of impingement appearing as a torque (turning force) at the output or turbine shaft (get used to the idea of the input rotor being called the pump and the other the turbine, for this is common parlance applied to all hydrokinetic devices). Thus we have a transmission of torque without any mechanical connection between the driving and the driven members. They can therefore slip relative to each other, but this does not affect the most important feature of the fluid coupling: the input torque is always equal to the output torque.

The efficiency of the coupling is measured by the amount of slip that exists at any given time, in other words by the difference between input and output speeds in a particular set of conditions. Most of the time, fluid couplings operate at about 97% efficiency once they have reached coupling point (that is, there is a minimal 3% slip), but they are very inefficient while running up to coupling speed. So the designer has to consider very carefully what sort of behaviour he wants when matching a fluid coupling to an engine: if it is to carry engine torque at high efficiency and low slip, the coupling may have to have a torque capacity very much greater than what the engine can deliver. Otherwise slip will be severe and excessive heat will

accumulate in the coupling. Because of the straight design of the blades and the symmetry of the pump and turbine, engine braking is possible.

Now, let us move on to the fluid converter. In this a third element is added between the pump and the turbine, and the blades of all three are curved instead of straight. The third element is called the reactor, and it is fixed so that fluid flow from the pump is diverted: the fluid impinges on the turbine at a more favourable angle, thus amplifying the torque applied to the turbine. Actually the torque on the turbine equals the sum of the torques on pump and reactor, and the resultant output torque may be much higher than the input.

This is the principle of hydrokinetic torque multiplication or conversion, and it is used in construction machinery; but it is not suitable for cars. This sort of fluid converter is usually at its most efficient at about 40% slip, but the higher the efficiency the lower is the torque conversion possible and—more important—the lower is the efficiency at the extreme ends of the slip range where all the engine power is dissipated in heat.

The answer to this problem is to mount the reactor on a freewheel or overrunning clutch; then, the reactor is free to move in the same direction as the turbine, but it is always locked against rotation in the opposite direction. At coupling point, therefore, the reactor automatically removes itself from the circuit in which it can no longer play an effective part, and the mechanism acts purely as a fluid coupling with no torque multiplication. We therefore call it a converter coupling, but the motor industry evidently cannot be bothered. Nevertheless this is what you get in your

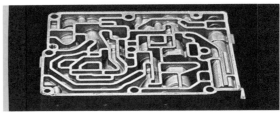

*Far left:* the Automotive Products torque converter; on the left are the turbine and stator, while on the right the pump carries the ring gear for the starter

*Near left:* in order to obtain the right gear at the right time, the gearbox oil has to be channelled through these complex passages

car's automatic transmission when the salesman assures you that it contains a torque converter.

In effect the best characteristics of fluid coupling and fluid converter are combined in the converter coupling. The transition from one function to the other, from converter to coupling after reaching coupling point, is a rather protracted business, for the curved blading necessary for converter operation is not altogether suitable for coupling operation. Furthermore, the coupling point is normally reached when input and output torques are equal, but at that point the output speed will still be about 10% less than the input speed. On the overrun some engine braking is possible in the coupling range, but not reliably below.

The full-load efficiency of a converter coupling is usually below 90% in the converter range, rising to about 95% or 96% in the coupling range. This efficiency is directly related to the product of the torque multiplication ratio and the slip ratio, from which it follows that when driven gently at low speed the efficiency is poor—which is why automatic gearboxes usually change up very early when the driver is dawdling, and why most of them tend to give poor fuel consumption. On the other hand, when input speed is high but the load moderate, efficiency takes a turn for the better and in these conditions can reach as much as 98%.

In industrial applications and for sporting driving, stall speed (when output speed is zero and torque multiplication is at its maximum) and the engine's maximum torque speed should be the same, and coupling point should be just a little below maximum power; but this would call for a heat exchanger to cool the fluid, so to save money in cars it is usual for the compromise to be biased in favour of restraint, as you can tell by watching the rev-counter during acceleration. Often an automated car is set to show a mere 2000 rpm during a stalled take-off (one where the brakes are held while the throttle is opened), despite the peak torque being developed at well over 3000 rpm. Change-up points are often premature, while it is objectionable to have to kick hard down on the accelerator to effect an early downchange, and indeed this kick-down facility is erratic, it produces jerky results, and it may be positively dangerous.

*Below:* this neatly sectioned automatic gearbox clearly shows the main components, including the two epicyclic gear trains and the freewheel in the torque converter. This box has three forward speeds and reverse, obtained by fixing the various components of the gear sets. The gears on the far left of the picture drive the speedometer

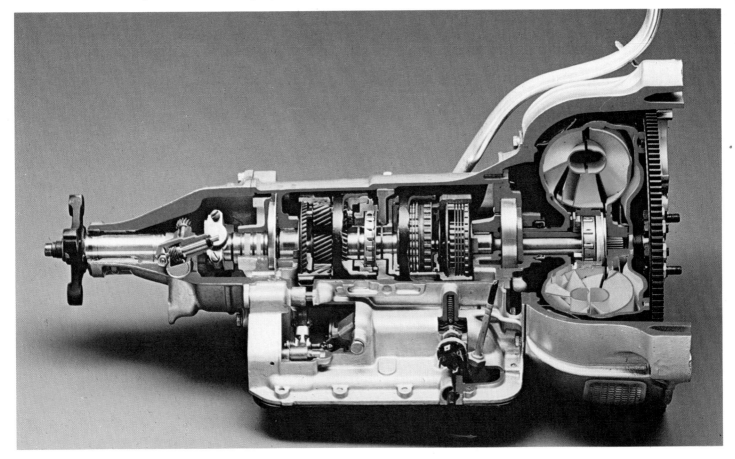

It is much better to hold or change down to low gear by means of an inhibitor facility such as the modern automatic box always provides. By means of a lever or buttons the driver is able to prevent the gearbox from changing up, or to force it to change down, the control mechanism ultimately modifying the action of the high-pressure hydraulics or (in rarer cases) the electro-magnetic devices controlling the clutches and brakes which hold or release appropriate components of the epicyclic gear train. These hydraulic or electrical systems usually monitor engine speed and load and vehicle speed in order to determine the appropriate selection of gear ratio. The number of gears is commonly three, though two-speed epicyclic trains were once fashionable and an increasing number of four-speed gearboxes are coming into use.

In any case there is no need to combine the converter coupling, nor even the simple fluid coupling, with an automatic epicyclic gearbox. An ordinary synchromesh gearbox will do, but there must be a conventional clutch between it and the fluid coupling if gear changing is to be feasible. This has been a popular combination in Germany (*vide* the NSU Ro80 and the Volkswagen 1500). The clutch pedal is generally made superfluous by a pressure-sensitive micro-switch built into the gear lever and linked, by an electrical servo system, to the clutch release, so that the friction clutch is disengaged whenever the gear lever is touched.

Note that this supplementary clutch does not have a lock-up effect on the fluid coupling. A lock-up clutch used to be a common addition to automatic transmissions: Borg-Warner incorporated one in their old DG series transmission, and General Motors did the same in an old Hydramatic transmission. Yet you can look for one in a Hydramatic and never find it: just as the original Hydra was many-headed, so have there been many versions of this transmission. Some had two fluid couplings, one always being full and operational, the other being drained or filled with fluid as and when required—which was in 2nd and 4th gears.

A later version was even more curious—if less disturbingly leisurely in its operation—for its single coupling had a free-running stator built into it; anchored to the gearbox output shaft rather than to the casing, this odd intruder gave a little torque multiplication (only about 30%) but kept drag torque very low.

It is also possible to vary the angle of the stator blades as is done in gas turbines. General Motors tried this in their Super Turbine 300 transmission peculiar to Buick—along with a five-element twin-turbine converter arrangement. As mentioned earlier, hydrokinetic converters and/or couplings can be combined in various ways. The multi-stage fluid converter, for example, is one in which the circulating oil impinges successively on two or more turbine members which are separated by fixed reactors. Its output characteristics are generally similar to those of a simple three-element converter, but maximum efficiency is always lower and overheating hazards are correspondingly greater. Maximum torque conversion is greater too, because of the extra stages, but maximum efficiency occurs at a lower slip ratio. In effect the thing is fine for conditions where part throttle cruising is punctuated by strong acceleration, as in the USA. A lock-up clutch is almost essential to provide direct drive and prevent runaway overheating in the higher speed range.

Another cunning trick is to divide one or more of the elements of a converter coupling into a number of smaller elements which can rotate at different speeds on their freewheels. In this way the characteristics of two or more converters can be combined into one called a polyphase converter, the advantage being

higher efficiency over a wide slip range and the disadvantage the sheer expense of making the thing. Split-drive devices can give better results more cheaply. For instance, by the mechanical shunt converter combination where the power flow from the engine is divided into two parts by differential gearing, one part going to a direct mechanical drive and the other through a fluid converter, both being collected on the output shaft by an over-running clutch. Again we find General Motors active along these lines with the Buick Dual Path affair, in which all torque was routed through the converter in low gear, but only two-thirds went through it in high gear, the remainder being transmitted mechanically through a planetary gear train. Buick claimed a high conversion speed for this, suitable for sporting or European style engines which developed peak torque at relatively high speeds.

This kind of facility, together with high mechanical efficiency in the crucial range, where the ordinary converter coupling is making the transition from torque multiplication to so-called lock-up, is also a feature of the latest type 4-element coupling. Not yet in production, it is called the Variable Kinetic Transmission and is the brain child of the same H. F. Hobbs who was earlier responsible for an efficient but commercially unsuccessful 4-speed automatic gearbox. We have seen 4-element converters before, notably from General Motors, but the extra element has always been a second reactor, to all intents and purposes akin to the first one which is located between the pump and the turbine. In the new Hobbs device the fourth element is a circulatory turbine that also goes between the pump and turbine, but at the periphery of the assembly rather than near the hub. As usual, the reactor is coupled to the output shaft through a freewheel; but the new circulatory turbine is connected to the planet carrier of an epicyclic gear train whose annulus is driven by the input shaft, while the sun wheel is coupled by differential gearing to both the output shaft and the turbine rotor. This gearing allows the circulatory turbine to run with the pump—faster when the ratio of input to output speeds is lower than 2:1, slower when it is higher.

So what? So the rate of fluid circulation can be increased to give greater torque multiplication when, for example, the car is being accelerated from rest. Not only is there more torque multiplication, but also it becomes possible for the stall speed of the coupling to be higher, which means that instead of labouring at a miserable 2000 rpm at full throttle with the car held stationary by the brakes (the usual technique for a full-bore getaway with an automatic), the engine can run at 4000 rpm or more and is able to deliver its maximum torque right from the word go. It gives a maximum torque multiplication of no less than 4:1, which means that a supplementary stepped-ratio gearbox should not be necessary.

Whether or not this latest manifestation of the art should prove commercially successful, it is clear that automatic transmissions are in continuous development and are becoming increasingly popular in one form or another. There remains the remote possibility that gas turbines or differential diesels might ultimately take the place of the conventional piston engine, or some other power unit that like them can do without a gearbox and all the other ancillaries and superfluities, clutch pedals included. The gas turbine is virtually an engine with its own automatic transmission built in; the differential diesel could almost be described as a transmission system with an engine built in. The long term promise of either may be debated, but the short-term success of the conventional automatic transmission is beyond a doubt.　　　　　LJKS

*Right:* during the 1930s, Auto Union and Mercedes, aided by the Nazi party, developed their cars into world beaters. With the approach of World War II, however, many races were cancelled. In 1939, using the V12 D-type, Auto Union managed to win only the French GP, with Hermann Muller at the wheel, and the last pre-war GP of all, the Yugoslav GP, with Nuvolari driving

*Below left:* Dr Ferdinand Porsche, designer of the incredible Auto Union racing cars, assists during the testing of the 16-cylinder P-Wagen at Monza in 1934

*Below right:* Hans Stuck's A-type waits on the start line at Pescara in 1934. With its enormous power and narrow tyres, it was a challenge for even the most fearless and talented of drivers

# A LESSON IN RACING DESIGN

Years ahead of their time, Hitler's incredible, state-aided Auto Unions
have established a unique place in motor racing legend

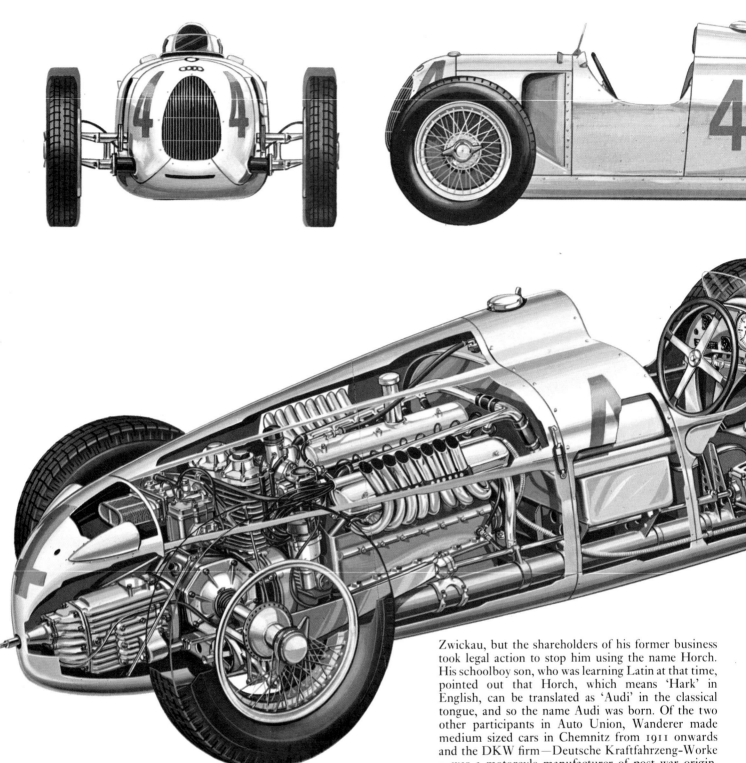

Zwickau, but the shareholders of his former business took legal action to stop him using the name Horch. His schoolboy son, who was learning Latin at that time, pointed out that Horch, which means 'Hark' in English, can be translated as 'Audi' in the classical tongue, and so the name Audi was born. Of the two other participants in Auto Union, Wanderer made medium sized cars in Chemnitz from 1911 onwards and the DKW firm—Deutsche Kraftfahrzeug-Worke —was a motorcyle manufacturer of post-war origin, making very small cars from the end of the nineteen-twenties at Ingolstadt.

After much rationalisation under the four circle badge of Auto Union, Audi and Wanderer agreed to make cars with many parts in common, including a 2255 cc, six-cylinder engine and a worm-drive transmission. The DKW segment of the Union went in for two-cylinder, two-stroke engines and front-wheel-drive cars which featured panelled bodies in a soft and flexible fabric in an effort to reduce passenger compartment noise. The 548 cc version cost only £149 when imported into England in the nineteen-thirties, the more powerful 684 cc engine version costing £10 extra.

The Horch unit produced a big, luxury car, which

FOLLOWING World War I, the German economy was, naturally enough, in a poor state and the once prosperous motor industry was very close to a total collapse. The more astute manufacturers soon realised this and it became almost common for former competitors to band together. For instance, after some co-operation from 1924 onwards, Mercedes and Benz amalgamated in 1926 and, subsequently, a rival consortium was formed by Horch, Audi Wanderer and DKW, which became known as Auto Union.

August Horch had made cars under his own name from 1902, but he was far better at engineering than finance and he soon lost control of his factory. Undaunted, in 1909 he started an opposition firm at

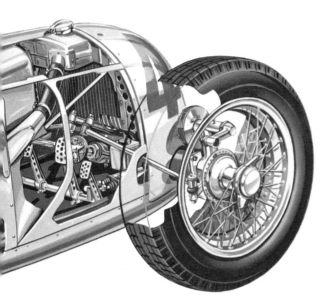

performance car, being very heavy and fitted usually with enormous limousine coachwork. The straight-eight was the most famous model of the period and this, also, was usually burdened with high and ponderous bodywork. However, a short-chassis version was made and, though this was still on the heavy side, it sometimes carried two-seater coupé or cabriolet bodies and was used by the Auto Union racing drivers.

The overhead-camshaft engine was twice increased in size, eventually having dimensions of 87 mm × 104 mm (4944 cc) and developing a leisurely 100 bhp at 3200 rpm, though the sporting coupés certainly gave more than that. In addition to the straight-eight engines there was a V8 of 78 mm × 92 mm (3515 cc). From an engineering standpoint Horch cars were of comparatively modern design, featuring independent suspension of all wheels, but weight was still the enemy.

In order to publicise the products of Auto Union it was decided to compete in Grand Prix races. For the origin of the Auto Union racing car it is necessary to go back briefly into history. Fundamentally, the concept of a car with a mid engine and independently sprung wheels comes from the German motor show of 1921. There, Dr Edmund Rumpler presented his brain child and, in a stultified world where car design had become utterly conventional, it became a fantastic step forward.

Dr Rumpler had already designed a swing-axle independent suspension for Adler in 1905 and, by 1915, he had patented what is really the modern system. During World War I he had also designed the Taube military aircraft and his 1921 car was basically an aircraft-shaped fuselage mounted on four swing-axles. The object of the exercise was to produce the ideal streamlined shape of a teardrop with the driver positioned in the nose, but with passenger seats in the wider middle section.

The engine was a six-cylinder unit, of unusual W configuration, placed at the rear of the passenger compartment and it drove through a combined gearbox and final drive to the independently suspended rear wheels.

Though Rumpler's ideas have now been totally accepted, at the time his car was far too advanced for the public and he was obliged to sell out to Benz in 1922. Benz had a fine racing history in the earlier, heroic days of motor sport, but, by 1922, they had become rather conservative. They saw the Rumpler design as just what they needed, not as a road car but as a Grand Prix racer.

The Benz Tropfen Rennwagen (drop-shaped racing car) was designed jointly, on the Rumpler system, by

*Left:* the 6006 cc, 16-cylinder, C-type Auto Union of 1936 developed 520 bhp at 5000 rpm. Usually geared for about 175 mph at most circuits, it could reach 215 mph when suitably tyred and geared. With its 5¼-inch front tyres and 7-inch rear tyres, wheelspin could be provoked at 150 mph, even on dry roads

might have seemed unwise when money was short. However, it earned some much-needed foreign currency and was thought to be subsidised by the German government to this end. When the Nazis took over in Germany, the new masters liked big, impressive cars and, while Hitler, Goering and Goebbels gave the Nazi salute from their Grosser Mercedes, the Korps-führers and Gauleiters travelled in Horchs of almost comparable opulence.

The biggest Horch was a twelve-cylinder, overhead-camshaft car of six litres capacity. It was not a high-

*Left:* Tazio Nuvolari, who was to become a works Auto Union driver in 1939, tried Hans Stuck's car during practice for the 1934 Czechoslovakian Grand Prix at Brno. Stuck subsequently won the race with this car, which was a 4368 cc, V16 A-type, developing 295 bhp at 4500 rpm

In spite of its 16-cylinder engine, the C-type Auto Union was a remarkably simple yet effective device. The forerunner of the modern GP car, its mid-engined layout was not copied by GP designers until the late 1950s, proving just how advanced Dr Porsche's original design was

Hans Nibel, Fritz Nallinger (later Director-General of Mercedes-Benz) and racing drivers Franz Hörner and Willy Walb. It had independent suspension all round, exactly as on the Rumpler car, with cantilever leaf springs and swing-axles. A major improvement was the fitting of inboard rear brakes and Rumpler's very deep chassis gave way to a light and liberally pieced channel-section frame.

The engine, which was situated in the middle of the car, with the driver up front, was built to the two-litre formula, prevalent at the time, and was a fairly orthodox twin-cam, in-line, six-cylinder unit of 65 mm × 100 mm (1992 cc). With twin Zenith carburettors, it produced 80 bhp at 4500 rpm.

In the 1923 Italian Grand Prix at Monza, the Benz single-seaters went well, but being short of engine power, finished fourth and fifth. As there was no more money to develop the cars—supercharging would have been necessary to make them competitive—Benz converted them to sports two-seaters and sold ten cars to private owners. Since they could achieve 100 mph in touring trim, which was then an unbelievable speed for a two-litre car, they were extremely successful in the lower grades of motor sport in the hands of their amateur drivers.

One of these Benz owners was Adolf Rosenberger, who was a partner with Dr Ferdinand Porsche in a small firm of engineering consultants. When it was announced, in October 1932, that there would be a new Grand Prix formula in 1934, both men saw the possibilities. This was to be the famous 750 kg formula, in which the cars, without water, oil, petrol or tyres, were to weigh less than 1650 lb, but the engine size was unlimited.

Rosenberger convinced Porsche that a modern version of the Benz was the answer and they got Willy Walb, who had been deeply involved in the design and development of the original car, to join them. In a very short time the team designed what became known as the P-Wagen. It was probably the simplest racing car that has ever been conceived, mainly in order to keep costs low. Admittedly, the engine had sixteen cylinders, but even so it was cheap and easy to make, with only a single camshaft at the centre of the V. As the cylinders were at a simple 45-degree angle, the single camshaft could operate the inlet valves through short rockers, with pushrods in tubes across the heads, while also actuating the exhaust valves through more rockers, the respective valves being at 90 degrees to each other.

Dr Porsche reasoned that he could save so much weight with his mid-engined car that he could afford to have a bigger engine than anybody else and this proved to be the case throughout the life of the 750 kg formula. It also meant that the power unit need not be so highly stressed and that moderate revolutions could be used. Such an engine could, and did, have a light crankshaft without fear of failure and further weight was saved by casting the cylinder block and cylinder heads in light alloy, with ferrous wet liners and bronze valve seats.

The camshaft was driven from the crankshaft by a vertical shaft with bevel gears at each end. Halfway up this shaft, a spur gear engaged an idler gear transmitting power to a large vertical Roots-type supercharger which breathed through a large twin-choke Solex carburettor. Like all other racing engines of this period it ran on alcohol fuel.

The transmission of the P-Wagen featured a five-speed, all-indirect gearbox with a bevel-gear final drive, the gearbox being placed behind the ZF differential as in modern racing cars. A twin-plate clutch was employed.

The chassis frame was extremely simple, two fore-and-aft steel tubes being united by one box-section and three tubular cross members. The suspension, which was novel at the time, was later used by Dr Porsche for the Volkswagen; that is to say it utilised very short, paired trailing arms in front and swing-axles behind. The trailing arms were on torsion bars hidden in the front cross member and there was a transverse leaf spring for the swing axles, with friction type dampers all round. The large drum brakes were hydraulically operated.

Dr Porsche's splendid design was immediately taken up by Auto Union. They wanted to compete in the 750 kg formula in order to advertise their products to the world and, in passing, to pre-empt Mercedes-Benz in the motor-sporting world. The racing workshops at Zwickau were put to work and the simplicity of the design and the construction soon paid dividends, for within a year, in November 1933, prototype cars were on test at Nürburgring. The team moved to other circuits for comparative tests and Hans Stuck was timed on an Italian Autostrada at 155 mph.

In March 1934, just before the first 750 kg race, Hans Stuck gave a convincing demonstration of the car's

potential by breaking many records at Avus. The circuit he used had two parallel straights of about six miles, with U-turns joining them at each end. Despite having to brake and change down for these bends, Stuck broke the world's hour record, a most coveted honour, at 134.9 mph and he took the 100 miles and 200 km records simultaneously.

By this time, the Nazis had taken complete control of Germany and were willing to give any assistance possible to Auto Union and Mercedes-Benz in the interests of national prestige. This backing was most valuable in securing the supply of scarce materials and it ensured the future of the Auto Union team. Sadly, it also involved the loss of Adolf Rosenberger, without whom the project would never have got off the ground. As the anti-semitic policies of Hitler started to manifest themselves, Rosenberger wisely emigrated to the USA.

The year 1934 was the first season for Auto Union and it also marked the revival of the Mercedes-Benz racing team. The 'Mercs' were of much more costly construction than the Auto Unions and they retained orthodox front engines. Like the cars from Zwickau, however, they had sophisticated suspension systems, so different from the classical cars against which they were racing, with their rigid axles and almost solid springs. Though both the German cars at first lacked reliability, it was at once obvious to the interested observer that these State-aided teams were going to be unbeatable.

For 1934, Auto Union fielded the A-type cars, with engines of 68 mm × 75 mm (4360 cc) developing 295 bhp at 4500 rpm. Like all subsequent Auto Union engines, immense low speed torque was developed, peaking at 2700 rpm, and in some races only two of the five gears were used after the start.

The first race was at Avus, where Stuck led until clutch-slip eliminated him. At this time, the team had no other drivers capable of beating the top Italians and so their best placing was third, behind two Alfa Romeos. At the Eifelrennen, Hans Stuck led but finished second after tyre trouble. In the French Grand Prix, all the Auto Unions and Mercedes-Benz retired, but thereafter they were to share the honours at almost every race. The German Grand Prix was a victory, and a very easy one, for Stuck. At Pescara he retired and the best Auto Union was fifth, but he led the Swiss Grand Prix from start to finish, with Momberger's Auto Union second. The team from Zwickau was second in the Italian Grand Prix and fourth in the Spanish, while

Apart from Mercedes, Auto Union's greatest competitors were Alfa Romeo. Here Achille Varzi, in the Auto Union C-type, and Tazio Nuvolari, in his Alfa, prepare to do battle during 1936

Stuck won the final race of the season, the Masaryk Grand Prix in Czechoslovakia.

For 1935, Auto Union enlarged their engine slightly to 72.5 mm × 75 mm (4950 cc) so that it developed 375 bhp at 4700 rpm, using 11 lb per sq in blower pressure. Instead of the plain-bearing crankshaft, with split big-ends, single-piece connecting rods with roller-bearing big-ends were adopted, entailing the use of a Hirth built-up crankshaft, a much more costly solution which the team could now afford. This was the B-type Auto Union.

Instead of using the frame tubes for cooling water, Dr Porsche employed them to hold fore-and-aft torsion bars, eliminating the transverse rear spring. The exhaust manifolds were replaced by sixteen separate short pipes, blowing upwards from slots in the tail.

To help the over-worked Hans Stuck, Achille Varzi was engaged as a driver, in spite of a prejudice against using non-Teutonic pilots. The cars were better but so were the Mercedes-Benz and, though many places were gained, outright victories were less numerous. Varzi won at Tunis and Pescara, and Stuck was victorious at the Italian Grand Prix, but at the Eifelrennen on the Nürburgring, a young motor cyclist from the DKW team, Bernd Rosemeyer, stepped into an Auto Union and had a tremendous duel with Caracciola's Mercedes-Benz, finishing second.

Rosemeyer was soon considered by many to be the greatest driver of his era, perhaps of all time. He looked extremely reckless, but he could use all the power of the big, mid-engined cars in safety. Some engine troubles followed the substitution of a new 5.6-litre power unit in mid season, but, once reliability was re-established, Rosemeyer won his first Grand Prix at Masaryk.

For 1936, Dr Porsche managed to get an even larger engine into his wonderful old chassis without exceeding the weight limit. This, the C-type Auto Union, had an engine with dimensions of 75 mm × 85 mm (6006 cc) and gave 520 bhp at 5000 rpm. An over-bored version, tuned for record-breaking, developed 545 bhp. With 5.25-inch-wide front tyres and 7-inch rear tyres, the handling problems can be imagined and wheelspin could be provoked at 150 mph on dry roads. The C-type was geared for 175 mph on most circuits, but it could attain about 215 mph when suitably tyred and geared, or over 270 mph when fitted with an all-enveloping body for record attempts. In short-chassis form it was a superb hill-climb car and Hans Stuck was the undisputed 'Bergmeister' (hill master).

The 1936 season was Auto Union's best year and after the first few races the cars were clearly superior to Mercedes-Benz. They enjoyed six major victories, of which the brilliant young Rosemayer won five. The 750 kg formula was due to finish at the end of the season, but, as so often happens, it was extended for one more year. Auto Union carried on with their old cars and were not quite so successful against Mercedes-Benz, who had a new model. Nevertheless, they won six races in a lengthened season and the race-going public had the ultimate thrill of seeing Bernd Rosemeyer win at Donington.

That was the end of the sixteen-cylinder car and Dr Porsche had ceased to be a consultant to the group. Accordingly, a new engineering team was assembled under Director Werner, with designers Dr Eberan Von Eberhorst and Ing Fuereisen, to produce a new car for the forthcoming formula. They chose the supercharged 3-litre category rather than the 4.5-litre unblown alternative.

Then, in January 1938, Bernd Rosemeyer was killed in a record attempt and Auto Union wanted to give up

*Above left:* Bernd Rosemeyer used this machine to set a record speed of 253.7 mph on the Frankfurt-Darmstadt autobahn in late 1937.

*Above right:* two years earlier, Hans Stuck piloted this streamlined Auto Union to a speed of 200 mph, again using a public highway

racing, but they were ordered to continue. The D-type 3-litre was still mid-engined but a de Dion axle replaced the swing-axle rear end, while side tanks were substituted for the central fuel tank. This allowed the driver to sit further back, with a longer front bonnet. The twelve-cylinder engine was entirely new, of course, and, though a central camshaft still opened the inlet valves, two separate exhaust camshafts were used, in order to cope with higher engine speeds.

The new cars were not ready at the start of the 1938 season and were unreliable thereafter until September, when the great Tazio Nuvolari won the Italian Grand Prix in an Auto Union. Nuvolari and the D-type were again victorious at Donington in October—a race that had been delayed by the threat of war.

For 1939, the 65 mm × 75 mm engine (2990 cc) was endowed with two-stage supercharging and developed 485 bhp at 7000 rpm in racing trim, though 500 bhp was exceeded during tests. War was approaching and races were being cancelled, but Hermann Müller won the French Grand Prix and was second in the German and third in the Yugoslavian, which was won by Nuvolari.

Zwickau is in Saxony, which is now behind the Iron Curtain and who knows what happened to the Auto Union racing cars? The DKW was re-introduced after the war as a three-cylinder, two-stroke, front-drive car and, after two-strokes became unpopular, the sole surviving Auto Union product was re-designed as a four-stroke under the old Audi name. Audi has now become a part of the Volkswagen organisation and that is presumably the end of the Auto Union story, though the famous four-ring badge survives.

It is curious that, although all racing cars now resemble the Auto Union with its mid-engine location, no designer copied the cars from Zwickau at the time. Only Rosemeyer could drive flat out in the C-type and people thought that it was because of the forward location of the driving position. In fact, it was Dr Porsche's insistence on front trailing arms and rear swing axles with friction-type dampers that made the cars so difficult to handle, though the narrow tyres of the period scarcely helped.

It is therefore all the more incredible that Auto Union actually designed a road-going coupé for sale to the public, derived from the racer, mid-engined and with sixteen cylinders! That it never actually reached the showrooms must have saved the insurance men a lot of sleepless nights.                         JB

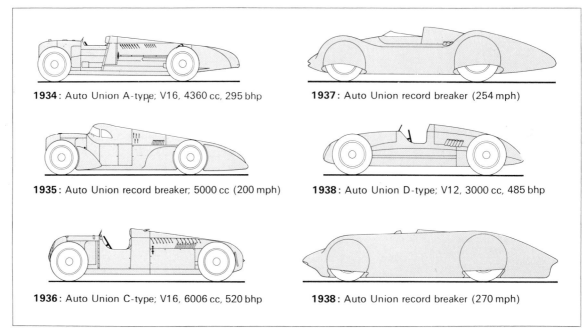

**1934**: Auto Union A-type; V16, 4360 cc, 295 bhp

**1937**: Auto Union record breaker (254 mph)

**1935**: Auto Union record breaker; 5000 cc (200 mph)

**1938**: Auto Union D-type; V12, 3000 cc, 485 bhp

**1936**: Auto Union C-type; V16, 6006 cc, 520 bhp

**1938**: Auto Union record breaker (270 mph)

# ALMOST AS OLD AS THE WHEEL

GENERALLY, any shaft bearing a revolving wheel may be called an axle. In cars, either front stub axle (the short shaft carrying a front wheel) satisfies this definition; nevertheless, the axle proper is a beam set athwart the car and carrying, at its extremities, a pair of wheels. Its origin is as obscure and almost as old as that of the wheel; its future is much less assured.

Despite the appearance of independent suspension of the front wheels (or even of all four) in some of the earliest motor cars, the beam axle was in almost universal employment until the 1930s, and for the rear wheels it remains popular to this day. In horse-drawn vehicles, the axle was very rudimentary in its construction and mounting; but the additional loads to which it was subjected in the motor car demanded a far better system, the evolution of which has by no means ended.

The first feature to be dismissed was the central steering pivot for the front axle: when the axle was turned, the front wheels each moved towards the longitudinal centre line of the car, so that the front became less stable. In the ultimate position, the axle would have been perpendicular to the rear axle and the car would have been about as stable as a three-wheeler. With the adoption of steering pivots or kingpins at the outer ends of the front axle, attention was then turned to the rear, and particularly to the means of transmitting tractive effort from the engine and gearbox to the rear wheels. The most usual arrangement for this, in the early days, was to have the rear wheels driven directly by chains. This meant that the axle could be fixed, with the wheels free to rotate on its ends—hence the term 'dead axle'. By 1905, Hotchkiss and Itala cars were experimenting with shaft drive to the axle, which was fixed firmly to the wheels, and attached to the chassis by leaf springs which thus not only provided the necessary suspension, but also the link whereby the axle propelled the car. This type of axle, which is subjected to tractive torque (drive), is known as a 'live axle'.

Attempts had been made by others to use a shaft-driven live axle, but this was usually kept in position by a 'torque arm' running parallel to the propeller shaft—or, later, a 'torque tube' surrounding the shaft and pivoted at the tail of the gearbox. At a later stage, the Hotchkiss type of drive was to become almost universal, but at the time of its introduction, its sole virtue (that of enclosing all the transmission mechanism, whereas the chains of the rival school were exposed to dirt and wear) could only be enjoyed at the expense of a noticeable deterioration in ride and roadholding.

The final-drive gearing (between the propeller shaft and the axle) in the centre of a live axle is heavy. The dead axle, with no more than a couple of sprockets adjacent to its wheels, was lighter and had a relatively high polar moment of inertia—that is, it had its masses arranged rather like a dumb-bell—and these properties of the chain-driven car allowed the use of fairly soft rear springs, well matched to those by which the even lighter front axle (bereft as it was of brakes in those early years) was suspended.

This soft springing allowed a comfortable ride and the best possible maintenance of contact between the

tyres and the road surface. More important still was the subjection of the live axle to torque reaction in the transverse plane: this reaction, generated in the final-drive gears, tended to raise the right rear wheel off the ground when tractive effort was applied, the most pronounced effect being at maximum torque in bottom gear. There were then no spin-limiting differentials (the differential allows one wheel to turn more quickly

Many early cars had their rear wheels driven directly by chain. This meant that the rear axle could be fixed, with the wheels free to rotate on its ends—hence the term 'dead axle'

than the other during cornering when the outside wheel has to travel further than the inside one), nor are there yet any which do not have certain disadvantages. In the 1920s, some cars were light enough to run with a solid axle, devoid of differential. Therefore the lifting of a rear wheel would allow it to spin, the action of the differential then allowing no useful tractive effort to be deployed until the offending wheel was returned to terra firma. This pernicious behaviour of the live axle was to grow more and more troublesome as time went on, as cars grew more powerful and lighter, until eventually it forced the abandonment of the live axle (at a time when chain drive had long been obsolete) in any car that might be a serious contender for racing honours or for roadgoing distinction in handling, traction or comfort.

The exceptions to this last rule were those cars which were comparatively heavy. What primarily governs the harshness or softness of a car's springing is the ratio of its sprung to its unsprung masses: the unsprung components (axle, wheels etc) should represent as small a proportion of the total as possible. If the entire car be very heavy, it matters little that an axle is fairly heavy; and in this case the advantages in simplicity, cleanliness, mechanical efficiency and consistent wheel camber of the beam axle may be preferred to those which make independent suspension virtually essential for a lighter vehicle.

An alternative—or rather, a compromise—that remained tenable for many years among racing cars (until 1959), and is still to be found in high-class road cars, was the de Dion axle. This was brought to prominence by its use in the 1937 Grand Prix Mercedes-Benz; but what was done to the rear suspension and final drive of that exceptionally successful and extreme car was what Horch had done in a touring car two or three years earlier, what Miller had done in an Indianapolis car in 1931, and what de Dion himself had done in the nineteenth century. The driving wheels were tied together by a transverse tubular dead-axle beam which ensured that they would remain perpendicular to the road surface at all times. They were driven from the chassis-mounted final drive by universally jointed (these joints make the shafts 'flexible') shafts in a way that conferred complete freedom from transverse torque reaction (wheel lifting). By this means, all the exaggerated angular changes typical of independent suspension, and all the inertial solecisms of the live axle, were successfully avoided. Only cost and space requirements prevailed against the de Dion axle.

As for the front axle, by 1950 it had become obsolete. Space at the front of the car was needed for the engine, now mounted further forward than formerly; and even where this was not a crucial factor, there remained the problem of steering shimmy caused by gyroscopic precession when one wheel rose over a bump and its angular deflection was transmitted by the axle beam to the other wheel (if a fast-spinning wheel be tilted, it reacts like a gyroscope by trying to turn towards the tilting force).

Many other criticisms have been levelled against the beam axle. It is often guilty of patter and tramp (hopping up and down or forwards and backwards on its springs) as braking or tractive torque acts through it. In fact these faults are not attributable to the axle itself, but to the means whereby it is sprung and located. This aspect of design is more properly studied under the heading of suspension, but it may be stated here that it is perfectly possible to mount an axle at front or rear so as to make it immune against all variations of steering geometry, wheel camber, tractive or braking torques, roll, toe-in or toe-out and migration of roll centre, up or down. As the mechanical complications and spatial requirements of independent suspension systems grow, in the quest for similar immunities, the possibilities inherent in the beam axle may yet come to be favourably reviewed.                                        LJKS

*Top left:* a 1903 De Dion Bouton with de Dion rear suspension, which comprises a dead axle, keeping the wheels vertical, and separate drive-shafts. This system is now used on many cars including Mercedes Benz and Aston Martin

*Top right:* a dead rear axle on the 1966 Lancia Fulvia Coupé. The axle is used to keep the undriven rear wheels vertical when cornering

*Bottom left:* the rigid front axle system was common during the early part of this century. The 1906 Serpollet was one of many cars to use one

# Beating the weather

DRIVING on dry roads in clear weather bears little resemblance to that on wet surfaces or in other bad conditions, be they rain, snow, ice or fog. Fair-weather driving could probably be managed by a child, but bad weather demands a far greater degree of skill on the road.

## Rain

During a long dry spell, rubber and oil becomes deposited on the road surface which is soon polished and smooth. As soon as rain falls, the water mixes with these deposits and forms a dangerous greasy coating which reduces the adhesion of a tyre dramatically. Under these circumstances, the road should be treated with great respect by cornering at vastly reduced speeds and accelerating and braking gently. Even when the surface has been wet for a long period

In foggy conditions, even headlights seem very dim, so it is worth making sure that they are clean. Special fog lights are a help, but they must not be used singly. Try to keep the car in front just within sight

and has lost its greasy coating, no tyre will grip as well as it does on a dry road.

It is in the wet that the tread pattern of a tyre comes into its own: on a smooth, dry road, a bald tyre, with the maximum possible area of rubber, will adhere better than one with grooves in it, but in rainy conditions, the tread is needed to disperse the water under the tyre and prevent it from aquaplaning (skidding over the surface of the water).

The condition of a tyre is especially important when the road is wet, as the depth of the tread grooves governs the limits of adhesion: the deeper the grooves, the more water can be carried away in a fixed time. In a deep puddle, the tread can only be effective until the water is as deep as the grooves; when this situation is reached, then aquaplaning is likely to set in.

When starting from a standstill, or accelerating in the low gears, use the clutch gently and avoid feeding too much torque (turning effect) to the driving wheels. In the absence of a limited-slip differential, one wheel will tend to spin rather than both, so that the car will be pushed off its intended line, something which, in traffic, can be very dangerous.

If the steering feels light while you are negotiating a bend, then you should slow down, as you are likely to lose all control if you persevere. Try and avoid any violent steering or braking actions in wet conditions, as these tend to provoke skidding. Use the gears as much as possible when slowing down, as this imparts an even retardation to the forward motion of the vehicle. Always leave a generous distance between yourself and the car in front to allow for the reduced tyre adhesion when braking. If the road ahead appears to be be flooded, slow down to a crawl before passing through the water, remembering to warn the driver behind of your intention.

If you do have to drive through flooding or you are cruising along a wet road such as a motorway, make sure that the brakes are working, either immediately after traversing the flood, or every few miles, on a motorway. A film of water between the brake pads or shoes and the discs or drum acts as a lubricant, so that the brakes may lose their efficiency until the water has evaporated or been wiped off.

To overcome this problem, should it arise, press the brake pedal intermittently until the full effect returns. Once again, be careful not to cause danger to any following drivers.

On a wet day, it is worth wiping the soles of your shoes before you drive, otherwise you may find your feet slipping off the pedals. A quick wipe on the carpet or a piece of cloth is sufficient.

A car windscreen becomes greasy and fly-spattered during dry weather, especially in summer, so as soon as the wipers are operated, visibility is hopelessly impaired. The answer is to add a special solvent to the windscreen washer reservoir—washing up liquid will do as a temporary measure, although it tends to clog the valve and jets in the system.

During heavy or incessant rainfall, it is quite common for the engine to start misfiring or to break-down altogether. This is usually caused by water entering the ignition system and short-circuiting the supply to the spark plugs. Should this happen to you, remove the distributor cap (it is from this that wires lead to the spark plugs) and wipe out the inside with a dry cloth. If the engine still does not start or run properly, then the terminals on the ignition coil will have to be dried (the ignition coil is also connected to the distributor cap by a wire). There are some special liquids on the market which, when sprayed on the ignition system, will dry it out. If your car is prone to

this sort of trouble, then it is worth carrying a can in the boot.

## Snow and Ice

Several of the precautions taken on wet roads apply to freezing conditions too. A light covering of snow on the road surface will be turned into water as the tyres pass over it, the friction causing a rise in temperature. In this case, the conditions can be treated exactly as for rain, bearing in mind that there may be ice lying under the snow, if the temperature is below freezing point.

As the temperature drops and the snow lies thicker, then the weight of a car passing over it will probably squash it into a hard mass which will become very slippery indeed due to the surface melting under the friction and forming a lubricating layer.

In these conditions, it is very difficult, with ordinary tyres, to control steering, braking or accelerating with any effect. Drive very slowly, braking and accelerating as little as possible and very gently and avoiding any quick moving of the steering wheel. If the car does start sliding, steer as far as possible in the direction of the slide, thereby giving the tyres a chance to regain their tenuous grip.

A front-wheel-drive car is, for two reasons, far better off in ice or snow than one with rear-wheel drive: first, the front-wheel-drive car will always tend to travel in the direction of the steering wheels, when under power, whereas the rear-drive car is inclined to go straight on; second, the driven front wheels try and lift out of trouble due to the drag from the back, while rear-wheel drive pushes the driven wheels down in an effort to overcome the friction at the front.

When starting off, with either layout, use a high gear such as second or third, so that the amount of torque being fed to the driving wheels is reduced, thus giving the wheels less chance to spin. If the car will not move, try rocking it by applying torque gently in forward and reverse gears alternately: this may build up enough momentum to overcome any obstruction. Failing this, remove rubber mats from inside the car, if there are any, and place them in front of the driving wheels and as far under them as possible. In the absence of mats, try and find a piece of heavy cloth, some wood or cardboard or some twigs and branches. A few willing pushers are a great help in these circumstances, rocking the car backwards and forwards as the power is applied.

With a rear-wheel-drive vehicle, always try and keep the steering wheels straight until under way, so that the car isn't trying to corner while it is attempting to get started.

The best way of avoiding trouble in snow or ice is to use special tyres or to fit chains to your ordinary tyres. There are two or three types of winter or snow tyre available: some are ordinary tyres, radial or cross-ply, with very pronounced tread patterns which do not clog easily; others are fitted with special studs which dig into the snow or ice and grip firmly—rather like a football boot in mud. In fact, both these types are equally suitable in muddy conditions, where it is easy to get a vehicle stuck. Chains are specially made to wrap round the circumference of a tyre, cross pieces acting like extra-large studs.

Special compounds are now available which can be sprayed on to snow round a car wheel, melting the snow and allowing the tyre to grip the road.

When it is actually snowing, vision can be impaired to a level comparable with a pea-soup fog, in which case good fog lamps are preferable to head lamps whose light reflects into the driver's face. Keep well back

*Far right, above:* the steering, braking and accelerating capabilities of a car are vastly reduced in the wet, so it is essential to make all these actions as gentle as possible in order to avoid provoking a skid

*Far right, below:* when conditions are icy, any fog tends to freeze: it contains minute particles of ice in suspension. This is extremely dangerous because it forms an opaque icy coating on the windscreen, obscuring vision

*Near right:* buses are just as susceptible to bad weather as cars, and the drivers have to follow the same rules. If you encounter a flood of this sort, drive through it slowly, in a low gear, and test the brakes as soon as you are through

*Below:* when heavy snow is falling, it tends to become impacted at each end of the wiper stroke, blocking vision. As can be seen, it also does its best to prevent the lights from being any use

from the car in front, in case its driver suddenly sees an obstruction ahead (dry-weather stopping distances can be multiplied up to ten times on ice).

It may be necessary to stop and clear the windscreen every so often during a snow-storm, because the wipers tend to impact the snow at each end of their sweep, which, as a result, becomes gradually smaller. If you do have to stop, for any reason, do so on either a level stretch or a downward sloping hill, to give the maximum chance of restarting without difficulty. It is better to keep going slowly, in a hold-up, than to speed on for a few yards and then stop.

As with rain, snow can cause trouble in the ignition system: the same cures apply. There is an added hazard of the cooling water freezing, but as long as the correct amount of a good-quality anti-freeze is added, this will not occur. Should you get caught out, refrain from starting the engine as this may lead to a cracked cylinder block or radiator. Pour hot water over the engine and radiator (keeping it out of the oil and, if possible, the ignition system), until the water in the radiator has thawed. Put in anti-freeze immediately as it is quite possible for the water to freeze again in the radiator as the car begins to move through the very cold air.

Never add radiator anti-freeze to the windscreen-washer water, because it attacks the paintwork of the car. Purpose-made anti-freezes are available, but a little methylated spirit will lower the freezing point of water by a few degrees.

## Fog

The main rule about driving in fog is to keep within your limits of sight. If you are doubtful about whether or not you could stop in an emergency without hitting the driver in front, and you are as far away from him as you can be without losing sight of him, then you should slow down.

Make sure your lights are all clean—don't forget your tail lights—and keep the windscreen dry and free of smears. Fog lights give better penetration than headlights, because the top of the beam is cut off to prevent reflection from the fog. Don't forget that it is illegal to use one fog light on its own; you must have a pair, or use one in conjunction with the headlights.

Extra bright rear lights are a very good idea for helping the driver behind to stop his car before it hits yours. It is always helpful to follow another car, as long as there is sufficient distance to stop.

If you are alone on the road, follow either the near-side kerb, watching carefully for parked vehicles, or follow the white line and cat's-eyes in the middle of the road. Leaning forward and peering through the windscreen will not help at all, as long as the screen is clean. In fact, you will have better sideways vision if you sit back in your seat—opening a side window can be helpful because it lets in outside noise.

Do your utmost to avoid overtaking in fog. It is far safer simply to follow another vehicle at a safe distance. Never try and hurry—in the long run it can only lead to trouble. IW

# ALL BODY AND BATTERIES

From two-seater runabouts to luxury broughams for the King of Siam—the Baker Motor Vehicle Co was the most enterprising and important of early American electric car makers

*Above:* one of Baker's first battery cars was this two-seater runabout produced around the turn of this century. It was little more than a battery box and motor on a lightly sprung frame and featured tiller steering, solid tyres and chain drive

ELECTRIC CARS were among the most elegant vehicles of their age. In 1909, the Baker Motor Vehicle Co, of Cleveland, Ohio, supplied an electric-powered brougham to the King of Siam. The body and running gear were finished in ivory, the folding top was of specially enamelled white leather, and the dashboard and wings were covered in white patent leather, the side panels and the front being emblazoned in silver with the royal crest. The car was upholstered in 'a delicate pale-green broadcloth, the royal color of Siam, with silver-grey Persian broad lace tapestry, puff rolls, and silver-grey silk cord and seaming lace'. All the metal parts were silver plated, with special silver lamps and meter case, the lever handles were of pearl, and the curtain lights at each side and at the rear were of bevelled plate-glass. Also, apart from all this it was, of course, almost silent.

Baker was probably the most important and enterprising of the American makers of electric cars. The company was founded by Walter C. Baker and Fred R. White in 1899, the year in which Camille Jenatzy established a Land Speed Record of 65.79 mph in the electric *Jamais Contente*. The first Baker was little more than a battery box and motor on a very lightly sprung four-wheeled frame, but within months the company was making attractive two-seater runabouts for town travel, with tiller steering and solid tyres. Although the first models were chain-driven, shaft drive was introduced as early as 1902.

It was in this year, also, that Walter Baker made his first attempt on the Land Speed Record. The Baker Torpedo was not, in fact, built by the company. Although it was designed by Walter Baker, it was actually made from his drawings by the Electric Vehicle Co of Hartford, Connecticut. It had a low, bullet-shaped body, made of white pine covered with oil cloth. The driver and his mechanic sat in tandem, in a fully-enclosed cockpit with small mica windows. The car was powered by a 12 hp Elwell-Parker motor, with chain drive, rather than Baker's newly developed shaft transmission, to the rear axle. The motor was positioned behind the cockpit and the forty Gould batteries were placed some in front of the driver, some at his back, and some behind the rear suspension. The car, on its 40-inch disc wheels, was 18 ft long and weighed 3000 lb.

In April 1902, Leon Serpollet in Nice had set a new record of 75.06 mph in his steam car, and, in June, Walter Baker, with his mechanic C.E.Denzer, made an attempt to better this at Staten Island Boulevard, NY. The Torpedo had covered a mile in 47 seconds when disaster struck. Accounts vary, but it seems that spectators strayed on to the track, Baker applied the brake, one of the front wheels collapsed, and the car left the course, killing two people and finishing up virtually destroyed. It was repaired and exhibited in London at the Crystal Palace in 1903, but did not race again.

Baker's next attempt to build a record-breaking car was also in 1903. This was the Torpedo Kid, a lighter, single-seater car. The body was similar in shape to that of the Torpedo, but the cockpit was open. In September it broke several distance speed records at Cleveland, but subsequently crashed after colliding with a Waverley in a race for electric cars.

Baker Electric also played a modest part in military history. In 1909, the prolific arms inventor Dr McLean of Cleveland, developed an anti-aircraft gun with which he claimed he could pepper a Zeppelin at a rate of 200 shots per minute and a range of $1\frac{1}{2}$ miles. The gun was mounted on a Baker truck, but does not seem ever to have been mass-manufactured.

Meanwhile, the Baker Co continued to make their handsome broughams and runabouts. They were, of course, intended only for town use, since their range was only about 50 miles on a full battery charge. The 1910 limousine—which was built to look like a conventional combustion-engined car, with a false bonnet holding the batteries—had a top speed of 30 mph.

In 1914 the company merged with Rauch & Lang, another electric car manufacturer, and in the following year they took over R.M.Owen. Owen adapted the gearless Entz magnetic transmission which had been provided for the US battleship *New Mexico*, and produced the Owen Magnetic car, which was later to be offered in Britain by British Ensign. With America's entry into World War I, the production of electric cars by Baker, Rauch & Lang was reduced, but their manufacture continued until well into the 20s. Subsequently the company has survived as makers of bodywork and electronic equipment.                          BI

# DISPENSING WITH VIBRATION

A great deal of power can be absorbed by vibration of a car's moving parts; balancing releases this power to drive the wheels and propel the car with greater efficiency

## STATIC BALANCING

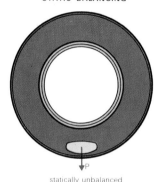

A mass P, concentrated at one point on a tyre and wheel, will naturally fall to the bottom if the wheel is free to turn

*vibrating*

When the wheel is spun, the mass P sets up a centrifugal force which causes the wheel to vibrate up and down on its suspension

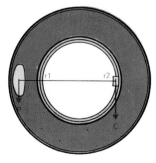

*statically balanced*

A counterweight C, fitted to the opposite side of the wheel, will counteract this tendency, provided the products of mass and distance from the wheel's centre are equal ($Pr_1 = Cr_2$)

## DYNAMIC BALANCING

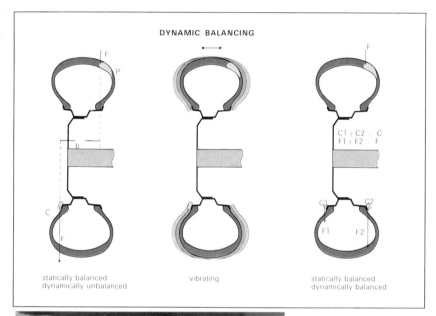

$$C_1 + C_2 = C$$
$$F_1 + F_2 = F$$

statically balanced
dynamically unbalanced

vibrating

statically balanced
dynamically balanced

The weight P and the counterweight C generate equal and opposite centrifugal forces at a distance b from each other (above left). This gives rise to a couple Fb which causes the wheel to vibrate (above centre). Careful division of the counterweight into two parts $C_1$ and $C_2$ can balance both the couple and the centrifugal force (above right).

*Left:* counterbalance weights are fixed inside Formula One rims so that centrifugal force keeps them on. Only one weight is needed to cope with static and dynamic balancing, since the weight can be moved across the wheel's width

BALANCING is the elimination of out-of-balance forces which might cause discomfort to the occupants of a car or might impose severe fluctuating loads on mechanical components. These components could eventually suffer fatigue and fail. The great majority of vibrations generated within a car (as opposed to those generated by the road surface, for example) are the product of some imbalance.

The balancing of wheels and tyres is the most obvious case. It is seldom possible to make these perfectly symmetrical about their centres, so counter-balance weights usually have to be attached to the wheel rims to restore smooth running. Static balancing

## 2 cylinders in line

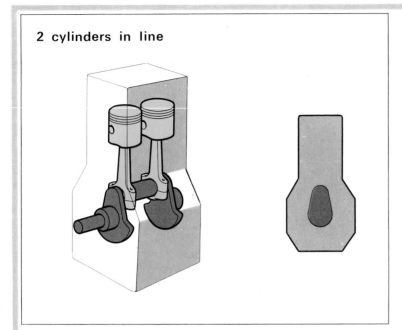

## 2 cylinders opposed

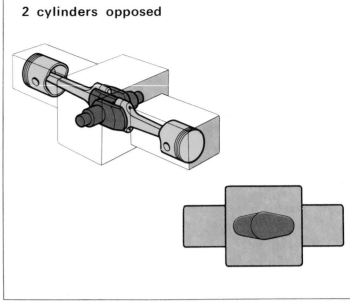

## 4 cylinders in line

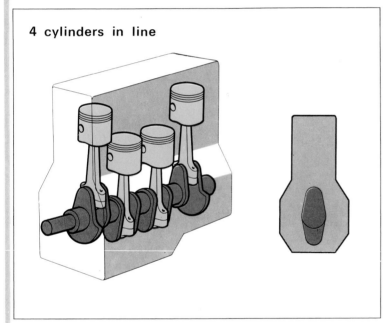

## 90° V4

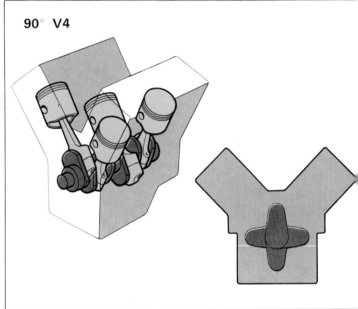

## 4 cylinders opposed

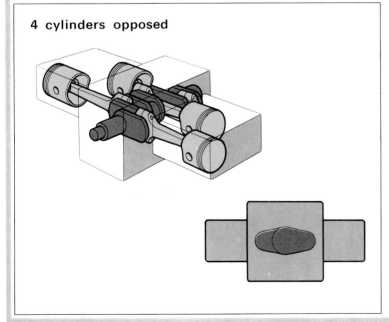

## 60° V6

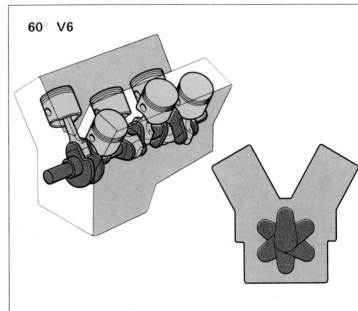

The drawings, shown left, depict the crank-shaft and piston layouts for various engine configurations. Some, such as the 90° V8 and the straight six, are inherently well balanced, while others such as the straight four and the V4 can never be perfectly balanced, although it is possible, by adding an extra shaft, to improve the balance. If the connecting rod were infinitely long, the motion of the piston would be perfectly harmonic and any configuration could be balanced by adding a suitable counterweight to the opposite side of the crankshaft

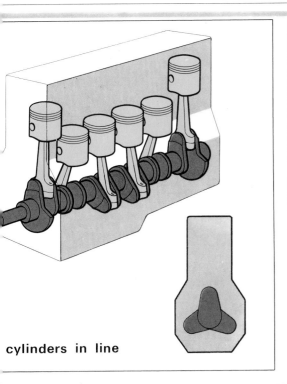

cylinders in line

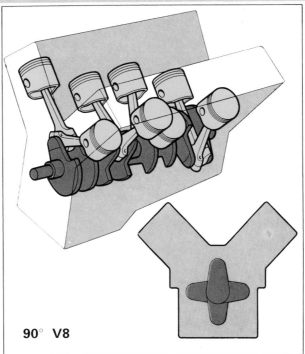

90° V8

8 cylinders in line

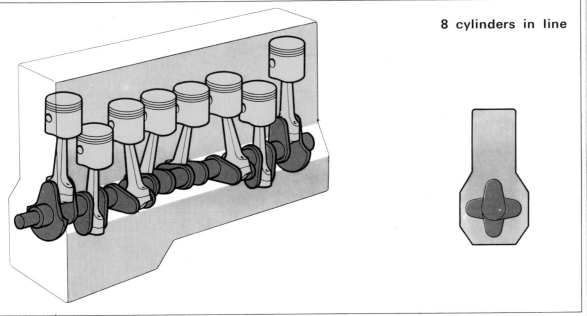

60° V12

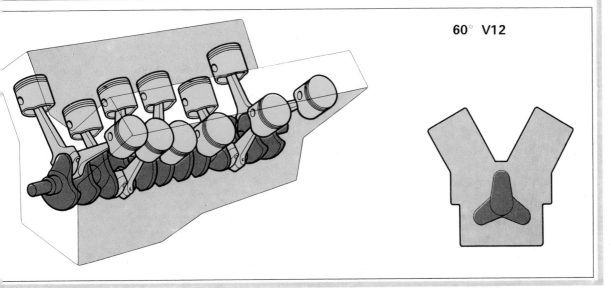

The crankshaft is balanced, preferably together with the flywheel and clutch, on a special machine which measures the amount of imbalance. Balancing is carried out by drilling holes in the heavy parts

is the simplest method: a weight is placed diametrically opposite the heaviest part of the wheel and tyre assembly. Dynamic balancing requires the correction of any tendency to overweight on one side, by placing a counterweight on the other side, after which a further counterweighting of the diametrically opposite point will be needed. On high-speed cars, even the brake drums or discs must be balanced—as must the propeller shaft, where fitted.

respect. Large-diameter V-belt pulleys may be balanced too, while the most meticulous manufacturers also balance the cooling fan and water pump rotor.

Engine balancing is a very complicated matter. The components which rotate do not themselves create much difficulty, but because of their association with various others which reciprocate, they may be subjected to out-of-balance forces and these cannot in all cases be completely eliminated. The design of the engine is of crucial importance: a single-cylinder engine cannot be perfectly balanced, nor can an in-line four-cylinder engine, while certain forms of horizontally-opposed or V engines present particular difficulties because the forces do not always cancel out.

The first step in balancing a multi-cylinder engine is to ensure that all reciprocating parts are of matched weights: all pistons, valve rockers, gudgeon pins and connecting rods must be of equal weight within their sets. It is, however, the connecting rod that is the source of most difficulty: were it infinitely long the angle change would be negligible, so the motion of the piston would be perfectly harmonic and even a single-cylinder engine could be perfectly balanced by siting a balance weight on the crankshaft, diametrically opposite the crankpin. With a rod of finite length, however, the motion is irregular: the piston acceleration from the top of its stroke is greater than from the bottom, for instance, and so any attempt to balance the reciprocating mass by means of a rotating weight must leave a secondary force still out of balance. This secondary force acts vertically (in the plane of the cylinders in an in-line four, for example) at twice the frequency of crankshaft rotation.

The secondary forces may virtually nullify one another, as in an in-line six-cylinder engine. In an in-line four they all act in the same direction and their cumulative effect is to make the engine shake up and down on its mountings. If these mountings are rigid, the engine will feel rough; if they are flexible, it can be made to seem smooth. Using the same 'flat' or single-plane, four-throw crankshaft in a 90-degree V8 causes the two sets of secondary forces to resolve into a shake that acts horizontally through the crankshaft main bearings; substituting a two-plane crankshaft, with throws at 90 degrees, creates the illusion of perfect external balance if heavy counterweights are applied to the crankshaft. There are many other engine configurations, a study of which would be extremely lengthy, but to illustrate some of the problems they pose, we might note that a flat six needs a six-throw crankshaft (which also suffices for a flat twelve), while a flat eight can be balanced with a four-throw crankshaft if two cylinders are arranged to fire simultaneously, otherwise an eight-throw crankshaft will be necessary. A twelve-cylinder engine may be made as a V engine with its banks of cylinders at 60 or 90 degrees (or 180, as already mentioned), a sixteen-cylinder at 135 or 180.

The illusion of good balance may be created by adding a supplementary shaft in the crankcase of an inherently unbalanced engine such as a V4, an in-line 4, or a 360-degree (parallel) twin: this shaft carries bobweights which generate an out-of-balance force. This may be arranged to counteract the secondary vibrations of the engine, but the crankshaft and its bearings remain subject to the secondary forces.

The crankshaft itself must be balanced with counterweights equal to the mass of the crankpin and, usually, the big end of the connecting rod, which has a virtually circular motion, in order to relieve the shaft and its bearings of bending loads. LJKS

*Below:* crankshafts have to be balanced statically and dynamically. The top pictures show a single-cylinder unit, and the lower ones a twin

Some of the most important balancing is done on engine components, since these operate at higher cyclic frequencies than any other part in the car. The flywheel and clutch may be balanced separately or in conjunction with the fully assembled crankshaft, which is itself the object of great concern in this

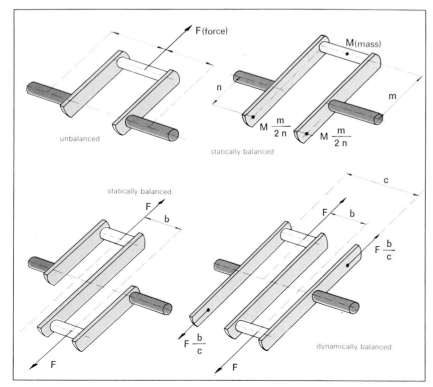

# Italy's handsome racing hero

Lorenzo Bandini leads former Ferrari team-leader John Surtees' Honda V12 at Monaco 1967. This was the race as a result of which Bandini tragically lost his life

THE FANATICAL Italian motor racing enthusiast expects much of his home born heroes, for nothing less than victory will satisfy these most demanding of supporters. In return, a successful driver will receive the sort of adulation reserved for footballers and film stars in other countries. The Italian enthusiast cares little for mechanical matters and is not interested in the fact that some foreign cars might be faster than his beloved Ferraris and Alfa Romeos.

Enzo Ferrari tends to pair a very fast foreign driver with an Italian driver in his Formula One team, with the result that the Italian driver often drives too fast for his ability. In the past, drivers like Luigi Musso, Eugenio Castellotti and Lodovicco Scarfiotti have lived and died in the shadows of team mates like Juan Manuel Fangio, Mike Hawthorn, and Chris Amon, while Bandini invariably had to play second fiddle to Phil Hill and John Surtees in the Ferrari team.

Despite this emotional and psychological handicap, Lorenzo Bandini captured the imagination of the Italian public as well as the Press, for he was darkly handsome in the typical Latin manner and behaved the way Italians felt their motor racing heroes should behave.

Bandini was born in Cyrenaica, North Africa to Italian parents in 1936, but in 1939 the family returned to Italy and he spent the war years in Florence. When Bandini's father died, at an early age, he was obliged to take a job as a motor mechanic in Milan, but he was fortunate in his choice of employer, for Goliardo Freddi was a racing enthusiast who helped the young Bandini by loaning him saloon cars for local events. His racing career began in 1957 and he soon graduated from cars like the Fiat 1100 to the more potent Fiat V8 sports car.

In 1958, Freddi loaned Bandini a Lancia Appia Zagato with which he won his class in the Mille Miglia. Bandini knew, however, that to get anywhere in motor racing he had to take part in single-seater racing. When the new Formula Junior was announced he rapidly acquired first a Volpini and then a Stanguellini. Although these front-engined Italian cars were no match for the mid-engined British types, which were setting drivers like Jim Clark, John Surtees, Peter Arundell and Trevor Taylor on their way to the top, Bandini gained some good victories in Italian events during 1959 and 1960, bringing his name to the notice of Ferrari who considered him for a place in his team in 1961. In the end Bandini, however, was passed over in favour of Giancarlo Baghetti.

Despite this setback, Bandini did drive in Formula One during 1961, as the Italian private entrant, Guglielmo Dei, provided him with a Cooper-Maserati. This was not a very competitive car, but the young Bandini placed it third in his first Formula One race at Pau in France behind Jim Clark and Jo Bonnier. He followed up with a third place in the Naples Grand Prix which gained him a drive in the Ferrari sports car team. At the end of the season he won the Pescara Four-Hours sports car race, co-driving with Giorgio Scarlatti. He also found time to win the Coppa Junior at Monza with his Formula Junior Stanguellini and, in the winter of 1961/62, he toured New Zealand with a Cooper-Maserati.

For 1962 he was signed by the Ferrari factory for both Formula One and sports car racing, but, with drivers such as Phil Hill, Ricardo Rodriguez, Willy Mairesse and Giancarlo Baghetti in the team, he did not get many drives. However, he finished a brilliant third in the Monaco GP and, with Baghetti, co-drove a Ferrari to second place in the Targa Florio. He also beat Baghetti to win the Mediterranean GP at Pergusa, Sicily at the end of this short but promising season.

Ferrari allowed Bandini to go in 1963 so Mimmo Dei of the Scuderia Centro-Sud offered him a 1½-litre V8 BRM, painted in Italian red, for Formula One races. The BRM had good handling, having given Graham Hill the World Championship the previous year, and Bandini enjoyed the English car, picking up his idiomatic English from the BRM mechanics who looked after it. Later in the 1963 season, Ferrari realised his mistake and signed Bandini as number two to Surtees. In the 1½-litre Ferrari he finished third in the Rand GP, fifth in both the South African and United States GPs and won the Le Mans 24-hour race, co-driving a Ferrari with Scarfiotti.

Bandini remained faithful to Ferrari for the rest of his career. In 1964 he finished second in the Syracuse GP and third in the Italian, German and Mexican GPs, as well as obtaining several good sports car placings. His team leader, John Surtees, won the World Championship in 1964.

Bandini's first Formula One victory came in 1965 on the rough Zeltweg airfield course where the Austrian Grand Prix was first held. He finished second in the Monaco GP, third at Syracuse and fourth in the Italian and United States GPs. He also co-drove the winning Ferrari in the 1965 Targa Florio, with Nino Vaccarella.

John Surtees remained with Ferrari in 1966 and Bandini was becoming fretful at having to stay in the shadow of a foreign driver, but he drove the new Ferrari to second place at Monaco and Syracuse and third place at Spa. Then Surtees had a much publicised row with the Ferrari team manager at Le Mans and abruptly left, elevating Bandini to the position of number one in the team. However, success did not come, for his best places subsequently in 1966 were a couple of sixth places in the Dutch and German GPs. The 3-litre Ferrari was much bigger and heavier than the fleet little Brabham which was doing most of the winning in 1966.

Bandini was now a prosperous garage owner and married to Margherita Freddi, the daughter of his first benefactor. He started the 1967 season as Ferrari team leader, very conscious of his position in Italian eyes. Victories in the sports car races at Daytona and Monza early on augured well for the season, as did a good second place in Britain's Race of Champions at Brands Hatch. Then in the Monaco GP he was running second to Denny Hulme's Brabham when his Ferrari touched the barriers at the chicane; the car flew across the road, mounted the straw bales, overturned and caught fire. The primitive firefighting equipment was unable to cope with the blaze and every time the flames appeared to be under control it would flare up again. None of the fire crew had protective clothing and could not approach the blaze. It was several minutes before the fire was finally quenched and the terribly injured Bandini was taken across Monaco harbour to hospital. By some miracle, he survived until the following Wednesday, but he finally succumbed to his injuries. He was 31.

Bandini's death came as a great shock to the members of the Grand Prix 'circus' and his death gave the first impetus to the great drive for safety in motor racing which is still being pursued energetically by so many people.　　　MT

OF ALL THE larger than life team of racing drivers known as the Bentley Boys, the most outrageously extrovert was Woolf Barnato, whose vast personal fortune helped the Bentley Company survive its mid-1920s financial crises; yet the Barnato millions dated back only one generation to the 'Babe's' father Barney, son of an East End of London shopkeeper called Isaac Isaacs.

Young Barnett Isaacs, armed with little more than his wit, changed his surname to Barnato, emigrated to South Africa and made a vast fortune in the diamond fields. When he vanished overboard on a boat sailing home from Cape Town, in the 1890s, his money went mostly to his two-year-old son, Woolf, born in 1895.

Woolf grew up to be a keen sportsman, with a consuming desire to excel at whatever he did. He was a big man who liked big cars and his first venture into motor racing was with a 48 hp 8-litre Locomobile he had brought back from a visit to the United States. He entered this for the Brooklands Automobile Racing Club's Easter 1921 meeting, coming third in the 100-mile Long Handicap.

By the Whitsun meeting, he had transferred his allegiance to a bilious yellow Calthorpe, replaced for the next season by Malcom Campbell's old 2.6-litre Talbot and an Ansaldo.

For 1923, Barnato changed to a Wolseley Moth, which he also ran at Brooklands in 1924, the same year that he set up Class H (7784–13,929 cc) records up to 300 miles at the wheel of his touring 8-litre Hispano-Suiza. In 1925 he bought his first Bentley, the prototype short-chassis, 100 mph 3-litre, which he had fitted with a pretty, boat-tailed, two-seat body by Jarvis of Wimbledon. With this car, which still survives, Barnato won several major Brooklands races and, partnered by John Duff, set a new world 3-litre 24-hour record of 95.03 mph in September 1925.

It was around this time that W. O. Bentley persuaded Babe Barnato to back Bentley Motors; Barnato, a natural gambler, sank nearly £100,000 in the venture, as a calculated risk investment—which failed to pay off. Though Barnato was prepared to risk money on this scale, and spent around £1000 a week on his lavish social life, he was parsimonious in small things, and expected full value for his investment.

So one condition of Barnato's backing Bentley

# The first of the

# Bentley Boys

was that he had his pick of the firm's products for his own use—he always had a brace of 6½-litres, one open, one closed—another was a place in the works team, which was revived on his orders.

But Barnato was no rich dilettante—on the contrary, W. O. Bentley regarded him as the best driver of the period, and one who never made a mistake and always obeyed orders. 'I think the danger of motor racing is greatly over-rated', commented Barnato, who didn't believe in life insurance. 'It is not as dangerous as it seems.'

In 1928, Barnato shared a 4½-litre Bentley with Bernard Rubin in the Le Mans 24-Hours race. As both were in their first Le Mans, theirs was the slowest of the three team cars, but the other two cars, driven by Birkin and Benjafield, were put out of the running by a wheel failure and a

broken oil lead respectively, leaving the team honour in Barnato's hands.

The Babe managed to overhaul his principal rival, Brisson's Stutz, which eventually dropped back with stripped gearing, but at the expense of a cracked frame, which caused the engine to lose all its water 40 miles from the finish. Somehow Barnato managed to nurse the sagging car to the finish—and win. He repeated the victory the following year in easier style, driving a 6½-litre Bentley. The team took the first four places in the event and the victory was celebrated with a particularly wild party at Barnato's huge country house, Ardenrun, near Lingfield, Surrey.

In 1930, Barnato pulled off the unique feat of three Le Mans wins in a row, after a spirited battle with Rudolf Caracciola's Mercedes; it was also his last Le Mans for the team, and the Bentley team's last race.

By 1931, Bentley's finances had become so strained that Barnato's advisers recommended that he put no more money into the company, which passed into the hands of Rolls-Royce.

Ironically, Barnato had bought a large holding in Rolls-Royce, not long before Bentley Motors was liquidated, and, by 1934, he was on the board of Bentley Motors (1931) Ltd.

In 1934, Barnato decided to sponsor a Brooklands track-racing car; his mechanic, Wally Hassan, converted Barnato's 6½-litre Bentley tourer into an offset single-seater, with the chassis underslung at the rear. On its first outing, it lapped Brooklands at 115 mph—and burst. Hassan replaced the damaged engine with an 8-litre unit with raised compression, running on alcohol. In 1935 Oliver Bertram took the All-comers Brooklands lap record in the Barnato-Hassan at 142.6 mph; the car was further modified in 1936, but was not fast enough to beat the Brooklands handicappers, though Bertram managed to lap at over 143 mph in an attempt to regain the track record from John Cobb.

Woolf Barnato died in 1948 and, despite his seat on the new Bentley board, it was one of the 'old school' Bentleys which drove to his graveside to pay the marque's last respects. MT

The Speed Six Bentley in which, during March 1931, Barnato beat the 'Blue Train', a famous French express of that era

# STORING A CAR'S ELECTRICAL ENERGY

Every production car in the world uses the well proven lead-acid battery to store its electricity. A little care can extend the life of this essential component by several years

A CAR BATTERY consists of a number of cells, almost always either three, giving a six-volt battery, or six, for twelve volts. Each of these cells is a typical electric cell, converting the energy of a chemical reaction into electrical energy. In a car battery, unlike a torch battery, this process is reversible. The chemical reaction can be reversed by passing an electric current into the battery, thus recharging it.

Each cell in a lead-acid battery, which is the type normally used in cars, contains two lead frameworks, the plates. The positive plate is filled with lead peroxide and the negative plate with spongy lead. These plates stand in dilute sulphuric acid, and the negative plate of one cell is connected to the positive plate of the next. When the cell is in use, that is, when it is being discharged, the lead peroxide, lead, and sulphuric acid change to lead sulphate, on both plates, and water. This chemical reaction produces electricity. When the plates have a complete surface covering of lead sulphate, the battery is flat. On charging, the reaction is reversed, and the lead sulphate is turned back again into lead peroxide and lead.

Immediately after charging, each cell has a voltage of about 2.6, but this soon falls, even on standing, to about 2.15 volts. When the battery is used, the voltage of each cell quickly falls to about 2.0 and it stays at that value for a considerable time, until the battery is nearly discharged. It then falls to about 1.8 volts.

A battery must, of course, have the correct voltage for the car it is to be used in, but merely having the correct voltage is not enough. If it were, one could join torch batteries to produce the correct voltage and use them in a car. In fact, a series of torch batteries would light only one of the smaller bulbs in a car. It would be totally useless for the main headlight bulbs and windscreen wipers, let alone the enormous demands of the starter. A car battery must be able to deliver a fairly large electrical current for some time.

Electrical current is measured in ampères (usually shortened to amps) and the battery's capacity in ampère hours (Ah). A smallish battery with a capacity of 40 Ah could deliver a current of one amp for forty hours before becoming discharged, or two amps for twenty hours, and so on. The capacity of a battery is not always exactly the same. It depends on the rate at which it is being discharged, so the capacity is usually given as, for example 40 Ah at a 10-amp rate.

A car with a large engine needs more current to turn the starter, and because the amount of electricity that can be supplied depends on the quantities of each chemical available on the plates of the battery, a large car will need a large battery. A typical large-car battery will have a capacity of 75 Ah.

When a car is in use, its generator or alternator normally keeps the battery more or less fully charged. However, in winter, when the lights may be used a lot and when the starter often has to be used more to get the engine started, the battery may become discharged.

It can be recharged by removing it, or at least disconnecting it, from the car, and connecting a charger that draws its electricity from the mains and converts alternating into direct current. The positive terminal of the charger must be connected to the positive terminal of the battery so that the electricity is, so to speak, forced back into it.

There are two basic ways of telling if the battery is adequately recharged. A third way, that does not work, is simply to measure the voltage across the terminals of the battery. The stable voltage of a cell before use is about 2.15 volts so it might seem that if a six-cell ('twelve-volt') battery records a voltage of 12.9 volts (6 x 2.15) or even 12 volts, then it must be fully charged or at least nearly so. Unfortunately, you need to know what voltage the battery can deliver in action, and if a battery is old or has been damaged, the twelve volts measured with a voltmeter when the battery is not in use will drop to nine or ten volts when it is. A simple test is to measure the voltage across the battery when it is in the car and connected, with the headlights switched on. If it still produces 12 volts, it is in at least reasonable condition.

A garage uses a more specialised version of this test. It has a device that consists of a voltmeter and a resistance: it is used to test each cell of the battery separately. The current from the cell flows through the resistance and the voltmeter therefore measures the voltage the cell produces when it is in action. Usually

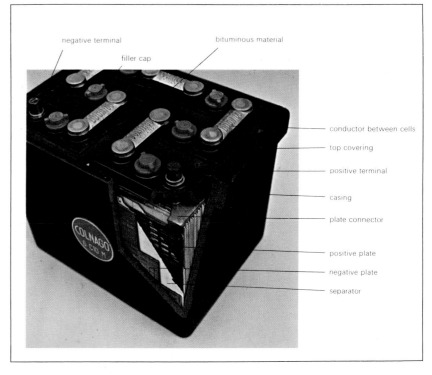

negative terminal

filler cap

bituminous material

conductor between cells

top covering

positive terminal

casing

plate connector

positive plate

negative plate

separator

This cutaway shows clearly how a lead-acid battery is made up of plates and separators, which are immersed in sulphuric acid. Cells are connected in series (+ to −) to give the required voltage

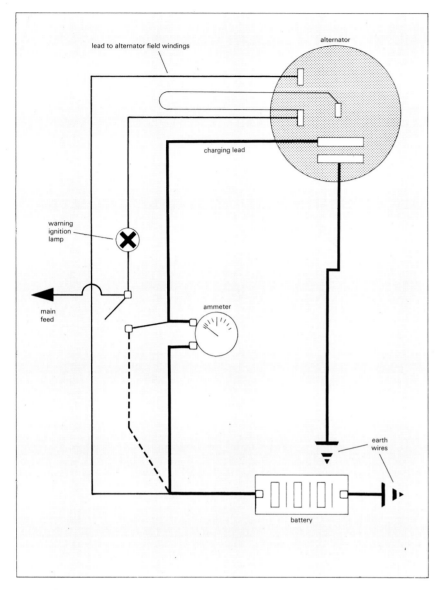

lead to alternator field windings

alternator

charging lead

warning
ignition
lamp

main
feed

ammeter

earth
wires

battery

*Above:* a circuit diagram
showing how the battery
is connected

*Above right:* two cells
from the beginning of
the century. The one on
the left has been dis-
mantled to show the
central lead electrode
surrounded by a paste
electrolyte and usually
contained in a glass jar.
The second electrode is
not visible. The capacity
was about 1Ah

*Right:* it is common,
nowadays, to use a
translucent or trans-
parent casing for a
Battery, so that the fluid
level can be checked
without removing the
caps. Most manufac-
turers have replaced the
individual caps with a
single, 'easy-fill' one

the voltmeter is colour-coded, so that the user can tell
immediately whether the cell is working properly.

A simple device that anyone can use to test a battery
is a hydrometer. This measures the density of the
liquid in each cell. As the battery discharges, the solids
on the plates change to lead sulphate, and the liquid

they stand in changes from sulphuric acid to water.
Sulphuric acid is more dense than water, so the
density of the liquid—its technical name is the
'electrolyte'—gets lower as the battery becomes discharged. The specific gravity, which is the most useful
way of comparing densities, of a fully charged battery
is between 1.28 and 1.30. The specific gravity of a
fully discharged battery is about 1.15 (the actual
values vary with different makes of battery). A
hydrometer will tell you the specific gravity, so that
you can tell if the battery is fully charged. Some makes
of hydrometer are coded and give direct reading of
the state of charge.

If some of the chemical on the plates cannot be
changed back into lead and lead peroxide, the battery
cannot be fully charged, and this is what happens as a
battery gets older. The vibrations of the car shake
material from the plates so that it falls to the bottom of
the cells; sometimes the lead sulphate appears in a
form that resists conversion (the cell is then said to be
sulphated), sometimes a battery is so ill-treated that
two of the plates get bent and touch one another,
which makes that particular cell useless. Any of these
faults will mean that the density of the liquid in the
cell cannot rise to its proper value and, while the
battery may still be adequate for summer use, it will
have to be replaced for the winter.

An ill-treated battery has a short life. One that is
properly looked after can last for many years. If a
battery is overcharged, either in the car or on a battery

charger, some of the water in the dilute sulphuric acid is split up into hydrogen and oxygen and bubbles off as gas. This mixture is explosive, so naked flames should be kept away from batteries that are being charged. The lost water should be replaced with distilled water so that the plates are just covered. If tap water is used, there is a risk that chemicals in the water will contaminate the plates. A battery should not be left in a nearly-discharged state, as the plates are then likely to become sulphated so that they cannot be recharged. In addition, the liquid in a discharged battery freezes more easily than the liquid in a charged one, and a severe frost may freeze the liquid and split the battery casing. Incidentally, a cold battery delivers electricity more slowly than a warm one, and people who live in cold climates often keep their car batteries indoors overnight. The plates can become bent if the battery is badly overloaded, but this is usually an accident and difficult to avoid.

The lead-acid car battery is rather unsatisfactory. It is expensive, it has a short life, and it is heavy, because the chemicals in it are lead compounds, and if it is to store a large amount of electricity, it must contain a lot of the chemicals.

The sheer weight of a car battery is one of the reasons that no successful electric car has been built. To go quickly, or a long way, a large number of batteries are required and in the end the car is carrying more batteries than useful load.

There have been attempts to produce different batteries, that is batteries that use different chemical reactions to generate electricity. Ideally, they would be reactions involving lighter chemicals. The NiFe batteries, as they are called, have plates of nickel and iron and have some advantages—they can be even more expensive, but they have much longer lives.

Almost certainly the battery of the future, particularly for electric cars, will be of the kind known as the fuel cell. In a fuel cell, one of the substances reacting is air or oxygen: the other is carbon or some other fuel. Fuel cells using hydrogen and oxygen have been fitted to space craft, but they have been unsuccessful on earth. The problem is that they are usually very expensive and need very complicated control gear. In one demonstration, a fuel cell was fitted to a pick-up truck. The electric motor was fitted under the bonnet and the battery under the seats, but the whole of the back of the truck was filled with the control gear.

The ideal fuel cell would use a freely available fuel plus air, and would run at ordinary temperatures. If such a fuel cell could be made, it could be connected to the motor of an electric car. Fuel cells are extremely efficient—experimental models have extracted 80 per cent of the energy of their fuels, and a fuel-cell car could be silent and non-polluting. Unfortunately, no-one has yet been successful in making a fuel cell of this type. TO

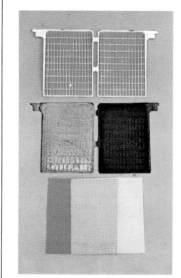

*Above left:* an ebonite container for six cells, showing how each cell fits into a separate compartment. The positive terminal of one cell is connected to the negative of its neighbour, thus multiplying the voltage by the number of cells

*Above right:* a cell removed completely from its casing. It has five positive plates interleaved with four negative ones

*Left:* the components of a positive and a negative plate. The lead frames or grids (top) support the active material of the plates, which is lead peroxide (centre right) for the positive plate and spongy lead (centre left) for the negative plate. The two plates are prevented from short-circuiting by inserting porous separators (bottom), of paper or plastic, between them

| Specific gravity of electrolyte | Condition of battery |
|---|---|
| 1.28+ | fully charged |
| 1.25 | 75% charged |
| 1.22 | 50% charged |
| 1.19 | 25% charged |
| 1.16 | almost flat |
| 1.15− | totally flat |

The specific gravity of the electrolyte indicates the state of charge of the battery. During discharge, the acid becomes diluted as lead sulphate is formed on the plates.
*The figures above are approximate and will vary from make to make.*

*Below left:* lead sulphate and oxide form if the top is not kept clean
*Centre:* a hydrometer shows a flat battery (left) or a charged one
*Right:* sulphation caused by lack of electrolyte (left), bent plates by over-loading (centre) and broken plates by inactivity accelerating sulphation

# TOO AMBITIOUS TOO SOON

*Right:* the 11.9 hp Bean was first shown at the Olympia Motor Show in 1919. It was a reworking of the Perry light car which was built from 1915 to 1916. It was available as a two-seater for £425 or as a four-seater for £450. Within a few months, however, the price of the four-seater had risen to £650

THE UNPRECEDENTED demand for cars after World War I inspired many manufacturers, whose munitions contracts had come to an end with the Armistice, to move into this potentially lucrative field. Some floated ambitious companies with projected production figures that were, even in those car-hungry days, blatantly over-ambitious; and among these was the Staffordshire firm of A. Harper, Sons & Bean Ltd, established in 1826 as metalworkers. With the coming of the motor age, they had built up a considerable business in stamped, forged and cast components, while, during the war, they concentrated on shell manufacture.

Their 1919 plans for motor manufacture included an initial output of 50,000 cars—20,000 more than the capability of the English branch of the Ford Motor Company, who were, at that time, Britain's largest manufacturer. In May 1919, to eliminate development costs, the company bought the jigs, tools and designs of the 11.9 hp Perry light car, of which around 700 had been built between 1915 and 1916. At the 1919 Olympia Motor Show in November, the public had their first chance to see the new 11.9 hp Bean—in fact, only a

*Above:* the 14 hp Bean Fourteen was introduced in November 1923. It was an enterprising design for the period, with dual ignition and four-wheel braking available as optional extras. Being strong and reliable, it was used by Australian Francis Birtles for many of his famous trans-continental drives

mild reworking of the Perry—which was available at a chassis price of £325, as a two-seater for £425, or as a four-seater for £450. Within a few months, the price of the four-seater had risen to £650.

A new parent company, Harper Bean Ltd, capitalised for £6 million, had been formed, controlling the activities not only of Bean but also of Vulcan, Swift, the Hadfield Steel Company, Birmingham Aluminium Castings and a dozen leading component and coachwork manufacturers. The aim was to create a British equivalent of General Motors, completely self-sufficient and producing an integrated range of cars and commercials to cover the most profitable sectors of the market. The group sold through an organisation called

the British Motor Trading Corporation, but its career was short and chequered.

Bean production was spasmodic; in January 1920, 100 were built. By February the figure was up to 125 and in March, the works at Tipton were capable of turning out 20 cars a day. Sales were not up to expectation and internal differences were wrecking the BMTC, which, by 1923, was selling only the imported Mathis and Cleveland cars. In a desperate bid to save the situation, aggravated by the collapse of the post-war boom, Bean copied the lead of Henry Ford in America and slashed their prices viciously in an effort to boost sales. The four-seater was now only £545 and competitive with the popular Morris-Cowley; but sales didn't improve, and the cruellest blow of all came early in 1921 when William Morris cut the price of *his* cars and watched the sales graph soar.

By the end of 1921, Bean were in serious trouble and were not even represented at the November 1921 Motor Show. Harper Bean Ltd withdrew their support, and a receiver was appointed.

The parent company's shares were bought by John Harper Bean and the receiver was withdrawn in April 1922. By now, the company had become distinctly less ambitious, and all thoughts of vast mass-production were abandoned. Instead, Bean aimed at the solid middle-class market, diverging from their one-model policy in November 1923 when the new Fourteen was announced. It was an enterprising design for the period, with dual ignition and four-wheel braking

available as optional extras. It was also competitively priced, at £395 for a five-seat tourer (the 11.9 four-seater was £345 at that period), which put it in the same class as the Austin 12.

The Fourteen, being strongly made and reliable, was used by the Australian Francis Birtles for many of his celebrated trans-continental drives, but despite such proofs of its capabilities, the Fourteen failed to save the slipping fortunes of its manufacturers.

In 1926, John Harper Bean resigned to join Guy Motors, leaving Hadfields in sole charge.

For 1927 they introduced a new model, with a 2.7-litre, six-cylinder engine and a new, squared-off radiator to replace the rounded cooler of the earlier models. The new Hadfield-Bean was an utter lemon, prone to sudden and disastrous big-end failure. A larger, 3.8-litre six was hastily developed for the untapped Colonial market, but proved to be even worse. Birtles drove the prototype across Europe and Asia as far as Hindustan, at a cost of several sets of back axle gearing. By the time he arrived in India the car, now rechristened 'Old Scrap Iron', was in an advanced state of dereliction. The Bean Imperial Six was quietly axed from the production schedule.

Now under the management of H. Kerr Thomas, President of the Institution of Automobile Engineers, Bean Cars Limited (the new title dated from the 1926 reorganisation) proceeded with a thoroughly eccentric marketing policy. At the 1927 Olympia show, they announced the new Fourteen-Forty ('entirely new

design, superb coachwork in dual tones') at £325 for a tourer, but continued production of the old Fourteen alongside it. As the older model cost less (£295 for the long-chassis tourer) and carried the same £14 road-tax on a larger engine (2.9-litres), sales of the new model were bound to suffer.

In any case, the 14/40 was yet another loser. Its power unit was no more reliable than that of the 2.7-litre 18/50 hp Six (which was taxed £4 more than the larger 14), and its worm-drive rear axle and poorly laid-out brakes were among the other trouble points.

Nevertheless, the old Fourteen had gone twelve months later; mercifully, so had the six, but even the new 14/70 Hadfield sports chassis, with Dewandre servo-assisted brakes, high-compression engine and raised rear axle ratio, could not save the company, and, in 1929, Bean stopped car production altogether. Their commercials, which had been produced along-side the cars since 1924, fared a little better, but in 1931 these were also abandoned and the company reverted to its former status as a component manufacturer. MT

*Top:* the Bean Fourteen-Forty Fabric Safety Saloon was fitted with an unreliable four-cylinder 2.3-litre side valve motor and was a total failure

*Bottom:* production of the Bean 11.9, introduced in 1919, was spasmodic and sales were not up to expectations. In addition, internal differences wrecked the company and, by 1921, a receiver had to be appointed

# REDUCING THE FRICTION BETWEEN MOVING PARTS

There are many types of bearing, variously suited to different tasks, but all of them are designed for the sole purpose of reducing friction

IN THE SIMPLEST CAR there are scores of places where one metal part moves inside another. In a complex car there may be hundreds—not only in the hubs and steering, the suspension, the transmission and the engine itself, but also in such oddments as screen-wipers, window lifts, door hinges, and even in the better sort of seat runners. Sometimes the movement is slow, sometimes fast; sometimes the rotation is continuous, sometimes intermittent; and sometimes the load is very heavy. For each case, there is a particular kind of bearing which will best serve to insulate the two parts from each other and allow that controlled freedom of movement without which they would fret themselves away in a brief paroxysm of heat and distortion. For each kind of bearing and for each application there is a particular form of lubrication although in some instances, no lubrication is required at all.

Dry (unlubricated) bearings are commonly found in the suspension and steering linkages of modern cars. Formerly such points were furnished with elaborate metal bushes which had to be greased at regular and frequent intervals. Later, bushes of porous bronze were impregnated with grease and could be left for longer. Finally, polymer chemistry devised thermoplastics such as nylon and ptfe, which could rub against smooth metal without creating much friction, which could manage without oil, or even work in the presence of water, and which, because of their inherent resilience, could be left unattended for many thousands of miles without deteriorating.

Heavier duty demands a bearing with no flexibility, and makes lubrication essential to prevent build-up of heat. In the wheel hubs and throughout the transmission, rolling-element bearings are the rule: the familiar ball bearing, or something inherently similar with cylindrical rollers to take greater loads, or tapered rollers to accommodate some combination of radial and axial loads. Inside gearboxes, rear axles and final-drive casings, rolling-element bearings manage well with a modest supply of oil; elsewhere, as in universal joints or wheel hubs, such bearings are packed with grease specially formulated to remain viscous when hot lest it melt and run away.

Hub bearings are going through an important phase in development. They used to be fitted in pairs in each hub, spaced as far apart on the stub axles as possible, but they took up space that was needed either for bigger brakes, or for the additional complications of front-wheel drive. The answer was to set ball bearings in asymmetric tracks, giving them a resistance to lateral distortion equal to that of a very much wider bearing or two bearings set well apart. These angular-contact ball bearings have now been redesigned so that their races (the annuli in which the balls move) serve as hubs and wheel carriers, making much of the old hub construction superfluous and liberating lots of very useful space, especially inside the very large bore of the bearing.

*Left:* a roller bearing showing the precision machined rolling needles. The disadvantage of this type of bearing is its unsuitability for motion at anything other than constant speed

*Below:* the Fiat 130, V6, cylinder block showing the four plain crankshaft bearings placed on either side of each pair of crankshaft throws. This arrangement gives the maximum support to the shaft

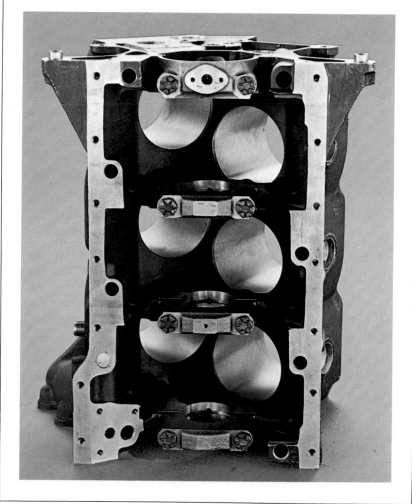

Although rolling-element bearings generate so little friction, they are seldom used inside engines. They are bulky, and finding room for them often means reducing the diameter of a crankshaft and thus weakening it. They overheat if fed with either too much or too little oil, making the lubrication system too critical for everyday use. They are expensive, and the built-up crankshaft assembly, usually necessary so that they can be threaded endwise onto each part, is costlier still. Split roller bearings are available, allowing a one-piece crankshaft to be used, but they are even dearer and call for exceptionally accurate fitting. Roller bearings do have advantages: they are fairly narrow, and they give good support against bending loads. Their gravest handicap, however, is their unsuitability for motions at anything other than constant speed. This makes them quite unsuitable for big-end bearings.

The trouble is caused by the angular motion of the connecting rod as the piston moves up and down its cylinder. This causes the relative velocity of inner and outer races (as it were, the crankpin and the big-end eye) to alter throughout each cycle; and the interposed balls or rollers have to change speed correspondingly. They accelerate towards top dead centre, decelerate away from it—but they are not suited to such movements, for their considerable inertia prompts them to try to maintain a constant velocity, in correspondence with one of Newton's well known laws. So they skid slightly in their tracks: and this is anathema to a rolling element bearing, causing increased friction, rapid wear, and a tendency for little flat surfaces to be worn on the rollers. Life is short for a roller big-end bearing, and death comes rather suddenly, and noisily.

Although there is something to be said for the use of rolling-element bearings elsewhere in the engine, if they are not to be used in the big-ends they are unlikely to be used at all: the cost and complication of providing two different oil feeds—a copious high-pressure flow for the plain bearings of the big-ends, a more meagre low-pressure supply for the others—are scarcely to be welcomed.

In any case, many engineers are convinced that frictional losses are actually lower in properly designed plain bearings. In a sense these still have rolling elements—but the 'balls' are now the individual molecules of oil that crowd between the inner and outer surfaces of the bearing. Such bearings are hydrodynamic: the relative motion of the shaft turning inside the bearing induces a wedge of oil to be drawn between the surfaces, creating a film upon which

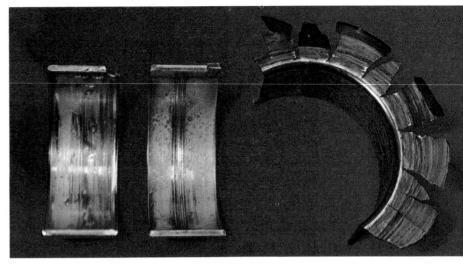

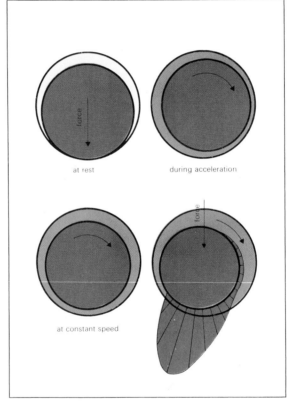

at rest

during acceleration

at constant speed

*Above:* the causes and results of bearing neglect. Furrows caused through lack of lubrication as a result of fierce acceleration when engine is cold (left). Gouges caused by debris from a blocked oil filter (centre). Seizure through complete loss of lubrication and resultant overheating (right)

*Left:* upon starting, engine oil is drawn between the surface of the shaft and the bearing to form a wedge which allows the shaft to float. The fourth diagram gives a graphical representation of the pressures exerted on the oil during running

*Below:* the placing of the crankshaft bearings in relation to the surrounding components

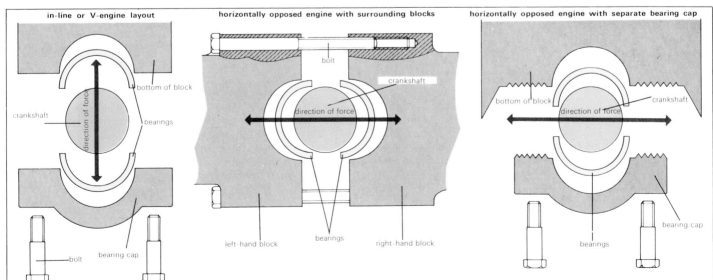

in-line or V-engine layout

horizontally opposed engine with surrounding blocks

horizontally opposed engine with separate bearing cap

crankshaft

direction of force

bottom of block

bearings

bolt

bearing cap

bolt

crankshaft

direction of force

left-hand block

bearings

right-hand block

bottom of block

crankshaft

direction of force

bearing cap

bearings

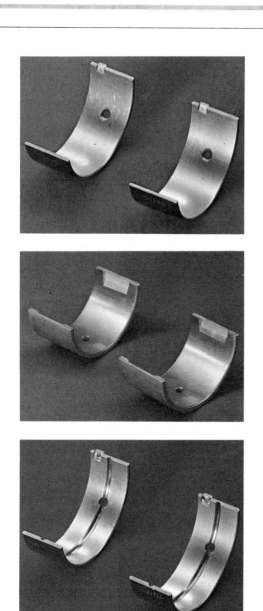

the shaft is supported. The action of the shaft is like that of a tyre aquaplaning on a wet road: the shaft planes on the oil, and the outer bearing constitutes an endless road. Of course, the oil gets squeezed out by the weight of the shaft and the other loads to which it is subjected, and that is why a high-pressure supply is necessary so that fresh oil may be forced into the bearing to replace what is lost.

The fresh oil must also be cool. When oil gets too hot, the necessarily soft metal of the bearing melts (or at least loses its strength) and bearing failure promptly ensues. As loads and speeds have grown steadily greater with the passing years, bearing materials have changed from the old lead-based white metal to sterner stuff that can take heavier loads without distortion and stand higher temperatures. Inevitably, these high-performance bearing alloys are harder; and since it is necessary for the shaft to be a lot harder than the bearing metal, the most advanced lead-bronze or copper-lead bearings can only be effective in conjunction with special nitride-hardened steel shafts. An overlay of softer material such as indium, so very thin that it can shed heat as fast as it absorbs it, improves

the performance and the adaptability of the bearing considerably, especially in the crucial seconds of slow motion and negligible lubrication when the engine is being started.

This form of multi-layer construction of plain bearings is now commonplace in what are called shell bearings, where the bearing is split into two semi-circular halves, each formed in as many as three layers superimposed on a strong steel backing strip. Credit for this invention has been claimed by many, but probably belongs to the aero-engine work of Ettore Bugatti during World War I. The design of such bearings today—especially in such respects as the location and size of the oil feed hole(s) and grooves (if any)—is based on very elaborate mathematical techniques; and in the course of their evolution it was demonstrated that many of the classical laws governing the design and behaviour of plain bearings were erroneous. Science, as its present practitioners will find in their turn, is like that. Indeed, current advances in lubricating oil technology promise to usher in wholesale revisions of bearing design, construction and materials, in the not too distant future. LJKS

*Above left:*
three types of crankshaft bearing. White-metal big ends (top), a similar bearing lined with a copper alloy (centre) and a white-metal main bearing. The groove in the main bearing allows high-pressure oil to pass from the block, through the hole, into the crankshaft, and from there to the big-end journal

*Above:* a selection of ball bearings. Like rollers, the balls can overheat if incorrectly lubricated, and they are mostly used to locate wheels and gears

# The man who tried too hard

JEAN BEHRA FITTED, only too well, the popular conception of a racing driver of the 1950s. He was short, stocky, muscular, completely fearless and covered with the scars from the numerous crashes which he miraculously survived—all except the last.

Behra, born in Nice in 1921, soon fell for the lure of speed on wheels: first he took up cycling, then motor cycling, his prowess on two wheels earning him the French motor-cycle-racing championship, three years in succession. Like so many motor-cycle racers before and since (including Tazio Nuvolari, Piero Taruffi, Jean-Pierre Beltoise, John Surtees and Mike Hailwood), Behra hankered after four-wheel racing and, as soon as organised motor racing began in Europe, following World War II, he was at the wheel of a Talbot which he drove to sixth place in the Coupe du Salon meeting at Montlhéry, near Paris in 1949.

In the following year he drove a Simca 1100 in the Monte Carlo Rally, showing his versatility by finishing third overall; he drove another Simca in the Le Mans 24-Hour race, but was forced to retire. Later on in 1950 he won his class at the Mont Ventoux hill-climb in a Maserati, and his exploits brought him to the notice of Amédée Gordini, known as 'Le Sorcier', because of his supposed wizardry with racing engines. He was the only man seriously to attempt to uphold French prestige in single-seater racing and he gave Behra a seat in his Formula Two team for 1951. He finished third in his first race with the Gordini, but the firm was perpetually short of finance and the cars seldom had the power to become competitive. All the same, Behra managed the occasional win, including a memorable victory over the Ferrari works team at Reims.

Despite a very bad crash at the Pau circuit in southern France during 1953, when he suffered severe back injuries, he was soon back in racing and continued with Gordini until 1954, which was his best year with the French marque as he won at Montlhéry, Pau and Cadours.

For 1955, he was signed by the Maserati factory team for Formula One and sports-car racing and was immediately successful, winning the Formula One Pau and Bordeaux GPs, as well as several sports car races, with the Maserati 300S. He suffered another crash while driving on the dangerous Dundrod TT circuit in 1955 and he lost an ear when the lens of his spare goggles cut it off. He was given a plastic substitute, with which he would often horrify the ladies by removing it at opportune moments. He stayed with Maserati in 1956, but had no success in Formula One, although he shared the winning sports car in the Nürburgring and Paris 1000 km races.

Although he again drove for Maserati in 1957, he was always driving in the shadow of men like Moss and Fangio, and early in 1957 he approached Raymond Mays of BRM to ask if BRM would provide him with a car for the Caen Grand Prix in western France. Mays jumped at the chance, for the team was short of drivers. Two cars were taken, one for Behra and one for the Franco-American Harry Schell and, despite a lack of practice, Behra won the race with ease, admittedly against modest opposition. Behra followed this up by leading a BRM 1, 2, 3 victory in the International Trophy race at Silverstone, in front of a 100,000 crowd. Behra became the darling of the British enthusiasts and his enthusiasm for the car endeared him to everyone at the BRM works. Despite his almost total lack of English he spent countless hours pointing out ways to improve the car and did a great deal to restore some confidence in the BRM team. He was contracted to Maserati for the rest of 1957 and managed to win the Moroccan and Modena GPs as well as sharing victory in the Swedish GP and Sebring 12 hours, driving the monster 450S Maserati.

Behra signed for BRM in 1958, but, in his first race for them at Goodwood, suffered a much publicised accident when the brakes failed and he collided with the notorious brick chicane at speed. He was badly shaken by the crash and his confidence had hardly returned when he suffered another brake failure at Aintree, fortunately without hitting anything. He suffered other accidents, including smashed goggles at Silverstone and a hair raising spin at Spa, and he never really got to grips with the BRM again, although he finished third in the Dutch GP. He fared better with the RSK Porsches in sports car races, notching up wins at the Nürburgring, Avus, Reims and Mont Ventoux.

Not surprisingly, Behra left BRM in 1959 and joined the Ferrari team. He won the Aintree 200 with the Dino 246 Ferrari, but, later in the season, he quarrelled with the Ferrari team manager Romolo Tavoni and left the team. By this time he had evolved his own Formula Two car, based on a Porsche sports car, and spent a great deal of time on this project; but he also drove an RSK Porsche sports car, being one of the quickest drivers on the circuits.

He took the RSK to the German sports-car GP at the dangerous Avus track near Berlin and, in the race on a wet track, he passed Jack Brabham at high speed going into the enormous high banking at the end of the long, fast straight; instead of rounding the banking normally, the Porsche suddenly shot to the top, hitting the concrete barrier. Behra was flung from the car, striking a flagpole as he was thrown out. The plucky, and often unlucky 38-year-old Frenchman died instantly.                MT

*Below:* Jean Behra at speed in a modified Maserati 250F during the 1955 Grand Prix season

# The password is determination

ONE OF the most determined racing drivers of all, Jean-Pierre Beltoise achieved the high spot of a patchy Formula One career by winning the rain-soaked 1972 Monaco Grand Prix at the wheel of a BRM. Born on 6 April 1937 and married to Jacqueline Cevert (sister of the late François), Beltoise has come up the hard way with more than his fair share of tribulation and injury.

Beltoise won eleven French national motor cycling championships before turning to four wheels, in 1963, with a drive in a 1-litre Bonnet. He had a few inconsequential races for the team and took a class win at Le Mans before suffering a terrible crash in the Reims 12 hour race the following year. He still limps and has a weak left arm as a permanent legacy of this serious accident. By the time he recovered, he found that the French Matra missile firm had taken over the Bonnet organisation and built a Formula Three car. Thus he helped to mould the late-1960s rennaissance of French motor racing.

Despite being only partially recovered, Beltoise won the French Formula Three Championship, in 1965, and went on to triumph in the prestigious Monaco Formula Three race the following year. He was then invited to drive the Matra-Ford Formula Two car and campaigned in several Grand Prix races with this machine in 1967. The Matra had to be fitted with extra ballast to bring it up to the minimum weight limit for Grand Prix cars, but Beltoise still finished seventh in the United States and Mexican Grands Prix.

He was given his first real Formula One opportunity in the 1968 Spanish Grand Prix at Madrid, deputising for Jackie Stewart in Ken Tyrrell's new Matra-Ford V8, after the Scot had injured his arm in a Formula Two incident. Beltoise led the race for several laps before an oil leak caused his retirement. For the remainder of the season he drove the Matra V12 for the factory team, scoring a very impressive second in soaking wet conditions at Zandvoort, but the team decided to withdraw from racing for 1969 in an effort to get their motor performing reliably. Beltoise also became European Formula Two Champion in 1969, driving a Matra-Ford.

For 1970, Beltoise joined Ken Tyrrell's team and drove Matra-Ford V8s alongside Stewart. He took second place at Clermont-Ferrand and nearly won the Italian Grand Prix at Monza after spectacularly outbraking both Stewart and Rindt into the last corner, only to run wide coming onto the finishing straight. Driving one of the V12 Matra sports cars, he scored the team's first major success by winning the Paris 1000 kilometres race at Montlhéry and, when Matra returned to Grand Prix racing with their works cars in 1970, was invited back to lead the team.

He led the French Grand Prix at Clermont Ferrand for many laps before being delayed with an oil leak and puncture and the best placings of a rather disappointing year were thirds at the Belgian and Italian Grands Prix.

For 1971, he was joined in the team by Chris Amon. This year started on a low note with Beltoise being held responsible for the death of Italy's Ignazio Giunti, after Giunti's Ferrari prototype crashed into the Matra which Beltoise was pushing (contrary to regulations) slowly towards the pits at Buenos Aires. He ran for much of the 1971 season with the threat of licence suspension and even criminal proceedings threatened, taking just a single sixth place in the Spanish Grand Prix at Barcelona.

Beltoise was dropped from the works Matra Formula One team at the end of 1971 when it was decided to field just a single car for Amon.

A controversial move, this was quickly followed by Beltoise signing to lead the multi-nation British BRM team which had just received major sponsorship from the Philip Morris cigarette concern. He distinguished himself by leading the first wet Monaco Grand Prix for over thirty years from start to finish, out-pacing acknowledged wet weather maestro Jacky Ickx, who freely admitted that there was just no way he could catch the Frenchman.

The rest of the year was indifferent for Beltoise. The works BRMs lacked power and he did not feature in the victory circle again until the end of the year when the unsuccessful BRM P180, which was subsequently abandoned, took a freak victory in the final Brands Hatch non-championship race. In Formula Two he was invited to drive occasionally in a March, but financial problems quickly terminated this arrangement.

He stayed with BRM in 1973, although the arrival of Clay Regazzoni and subsequently Niki Lauda demoted Beltoise to effective 'third string' status. It was a less happy season, punctuated by accidents at Monaco and Silverstone, although he was actually running second in the controversial and confusing Canadian Grand Prix until two laps from the finish, when Emerson Fittipaldi and Jackie Oliver passed him and pushed him down to fourth. In Formula Two he was asked to join the works March-BMW team for several races, but many of these clashed with his Matra sports car commitments and, when he did race, the BMW engines did nothing but give him trouble. He drove a Matra MS670 with Francois Cevert at Le Mans, but mechanical difficulties forced them to relinquish their lead and the car was subsequently retired.

Beltoise again signed with BRM for the 1974 season.                    NB

161

# THE BACKBONE OF BRITISH MOTORING

Now regarded as being among the greatest classic car manufacturers of all time, the Bentley epitomises all that is British

THINK OF the archetypal vintage car, and the chances are that you think of the 3-litre Bentley. Yet fewer 3-litres—around 1600—were built in the model's 8-year currency than the number of Bullnose Oxfords and Cowleys that left William Morris's factory during a single month in 1925, and you could have bought a complete new Morris or Clyno tourer for less than the cost of the Bentley's skimpy tourer coachwork.

Also, though it has achieved such legendary fame, the Bentley was no better and no worse than many other marques of the 1920s: it was just more fortunate in its choice of godparents—the *Autocar* writer S. C. H. Davis, who sang its praises in print and drove for the works team, and the *Autocar* artist F. Gordon Crosby, who designed its radiator and badge.

The marque's progenitor would, in any case, have been happier in locomotive engineering. Born on 16 September 1888, Walter Owen Bentley was the ninth of eleven children; he had served five years as a premium apprentice in the Great Northern Railway's workshops at Doncaster, only to decide that the financial rewards of a career on the railways were hardly worthwhile.

So he joined the National Motor Cab Company of Hammersmith late in 1910 at the recommendation of a friend, E. M. P. Boileau of *The Autocar*, charged with the task of keeping the firm's 250 Unic taxis running economically; but already he had developed a taste for fast motoring which at that time he satisfied with competition successes on Rex and Indian motorcycles.

In 1912, Bentley had the opportunity to go into the motor trade with his brother H.M. They bought out the partners of a moribund business that imported the French Doriot, Flandrin & Parant—DFP for short—into Britain.

The DFP was available in three models, the 10–12 hp, the 12–15 hp and the 16–20 hp; the smallest and largest machines were unremarkable, but W.O. realised that the 12–15 offered better potential performance than any of its competitors, and instituted a competition programme to provide the necessary publicity to boost sales.

On his first outing, Bentley broke the 2-litre class record for the ascent of Aston Clinton hill, in Buckinghamshire, and found that proven speed capability was a good selling point, even though keeping up a good competition record strained the meagre finances of Bentley & Bentley Ltd to the utmost.

But at speeds of 80 mph-plus, the DFP proved to have a weak point—pistons—and it was while W.O. was visiting the DFP factory at Courbevoie, near Paris, that he noticed an aluminium paperweight in the shape of a miniature piston on M. Doriot's desk.

Bentley had some full size alloy pistons made, found they gave more power and speed, and used them in a new 12–40 DFP Speed Model he had asked the factory to develop for the English market.

At the same time, and unknown to him, some Continental manufacturers were experimenting with alloy pistons, and the British scientist Dr A. M. Low had fitted a set to his Gregoire. But Bentley was almost certainly the first on the English market to use alloy pistons in a production model.

At Brooklands, an alloy-pistoned DFP racer proved faster than machines of twice the swept volume, and the model put up a good showing in the 1914 Isle of Man Tourist Trophy race, being one of six cars to finish out of 23 starters. Eight weeks later war broke out.

Bentley offered the alloy piston to the Government as a contribution to the war effort, was given a commission in the Navy and sent out to persuade engine makers that the aluminium piston was superior to those made of cast-iron or steel. First to make use of Bentley's discovery were Rolls-Royce, whose new Eagle aero-engine owed a good deal to the 1914 Grand Prix-winning Mercedes, which Bentley had found covered in old sacks in the basement of the former British Mercedes showrooms in Long Acre.

Next, Bentley was assigned to Gwynne of Chiswick, who were building the French Clerget rotary under licence; but the Clerget was an unsatisfactory design, and W.O. was anxious to develop his own aero-engine. In 1916 he was given the opportunity, as Humber of Coventry were keen to produce something more exciting than the bicycles and field kitchens with which their factory was occupied; in conjunction with Humber's chief designer, F. T. Burgess, Bentley developed a nine-cylinder rotary engine, the BR 1, which reached production status by late 1916. By the spring of 1918 a larger rotary, the BR 2, was being built at the rate of 120 a week for the new Sopwith Snipe fighter scout, but the rotary was an evolutionary dead end and, by the Armistice, the RAF had begun to concentrate on the fixed radial engine, even though their first choice, the ABC Dragonfly, was an unreliable and temperamental piece of machinery.

In their few quiet moments at Coventry, Bentley and Burgess had roughed out a few sketches for a postwar car that would take over where the DFP had left off, a car designed for fast cruising on Continental roads.

And after the Armistice Burgess and Harry Varley, formerly with Vauxhall, began detail work on this

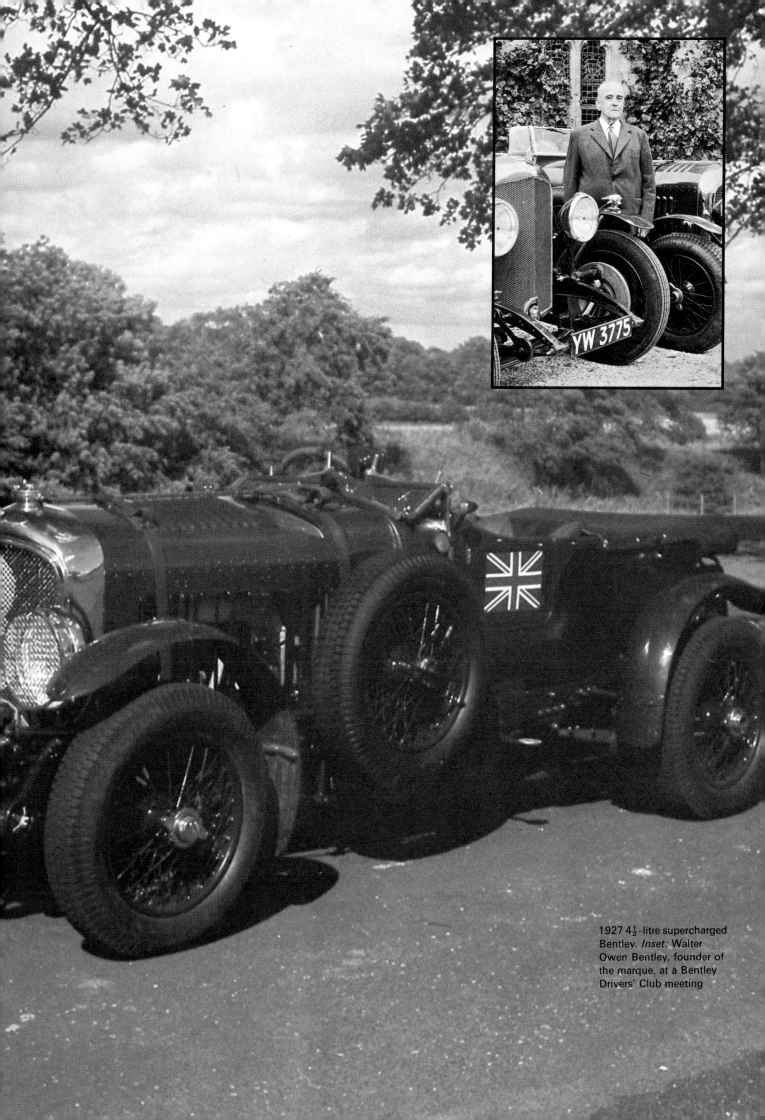

1927 4½-litre supercharged Bentley. *Inset:* Walter Owen Bentley, founder of the marque, at a Bentley Drivers' Club meeting

project under the leadership of W. O. Bentley.

Finance for the venture came from the sales of DFPs in the boom period after the Armistice, when annual profits soared to around £20,000, but, recalled Bentley many years later, 'to design and build a new motor car in 1919 without substantial capital was like being cast on a desert island with a penknife and orders to build a house'.

Nevertheless, in October 1919, ten months after Bentley, Burgess and Varley had started work, the first prototype engine was built and ready to run.

In its overall layout, the new 3-litre Bentley power unit gave more than a hint of what the complex power unit of that GP Mercedes, which Bentley had unearthed in the Long Acre basement in 1915, might have looked like translated into production terms. Instead of the separate machined-steel cylinders with welded-on water-jackets that had characterised the Mercedes, the Bentley had the cylinders cast *en bloc*, with water plates screwed on the sides and ends. But the vertical kingshaft, at the front of the engine, which drove the overhead camshaft was pure Mercedes, as was the layout of the valve gear and the four valves per cylinder.

The chassis, on the other hand, had definite affinities with the 1914 Grand Prix Peugeot, with four-wheel Perrot brakes and cardan shaft drive to the back axle.

The first prototype was complete enough to be shown at the November 1919 Olympia Motor Show where it attracted great attention and not a few hopeful orders, which Bentley turned away 'until we had something better to offer'; some time the same month the car made its first brief test runs. And almost exactly a year after the first rough sketches had been committed to paper, the first road test appeared, written by 'Sammy' Davis of *Autocar*; it was so enthusiastic that once again Bentley was besieged with orders which he felt unable to fulfil until the design was perfected, and the 'ear-splitting row' of the prototype refined.

At this point, Bentley could easily have found outside backers to finance the venture adequately; instead he decided to go it alone, bought a site in Oxgate Lane, Cricklewood, North London and built a small factory, where the next prototypes were built. Though a comparatively large staff was taken on, it was not until September 1921 that the first car was sold, to the wealthy young socialite Noel van Raalte, who owned Brownsea Island in Poole Harbour and who had provided much of the backing for the KLG spark plug business.

By that time the money was beginning to run out: for the rest of its lifespan the Bentley company was generally in financial difficulties, often quite unable to put aside enough money one week to meet the following week's wage bill.

Already W.O. had been diverted from his original aim, which was to make enough money with the 3-litre to enable the company to break into the family car market with a smaller, cheaper model. And the Bentley was certainly expensive. At a 1923 chassis price of £895 for the standard long-wheelbase touring model, the 3-litre was far and away the most costly model of its size on the market, with a price tag up to three times as great as other 16 hp cars.

By the time the model was ready to be marketed, its technical advances, such as four-wheel-braking, had been largely eroded as competing marques improved their specification; and the 1922 sales figure of 145 was hardly remarkable.

From the start, Bentley pursued an active racing programme in order to publicise their products: 'We were in racing not for the glory and heroics, but strictly for business', recalled W.O. in his autobiography. However, the first major event in which the marque competed, the 1922 Indianapolis 500, was a costly failure, for the car just wasn't fast enough to keep up with the locals, though it *did* finish.

The company enjoyed better fortune a few weeks later in the Isle of Man Tourist Trophy, held in pouring rain: Frank Clement came in second, just behind Jean Chassagne's winning Sunbeam; W. O. Bentley was fourth and Douglas Hawkes was fifth, clinching the team prize.

Sales picked up slowly: in 1923, 204 Bentleys were produced, but in 1924 3-litre output peaked at 403, the largest annual production of any Bentley model.

Much of the 3-litre's popularity was due to word-of-mouth recommendation and competition successes by customers, most accomplished of whom was John Duff, son of a missionary and born in China. He had bought one of the first production Bentleys, and took it to Brooklands where, on 28 September 1922, he took class records from three hours to 1000 miles at average speeds around 88 mph. When he heard that the French were planning a 24-hour race at Le Mans, he asked Bentley for backing for a solo entry. Partnered by Frank Clement, Duff managed to come fourth, in spite of a petrol tank punctured by flying stones and patched with chewing gum.

In 1924, Duff came first at Le Mans, a victory which set the pattern for Bentley's competition motoring,

though the 1925 and 1926 Le Mans events brought the company no honours.

Meanwhile, W.O., who felt that the increasing number of customers who wanted long wheelbase 3-litres with saloon coachwork were causing him to debase the models' sporting integrity, had developed a new, larger model for the carriage trade. This new six-cylinder was originally planned as a $4\frac{1}{2}$-litre, but a chance encounter between the prototype and the new Rolls-Royce Phantom on French roads led to the decision to enlarge this car's engine to $6\frac{1}{2}$ litres.

The $6\frac{1}{2}$-litre was introduced at the 1925 Motor Show; to cure the rough-running of the engine, Bentley had mounted it on rubber pads, possibly the first time this expedient had been used on a British production car (though in France Mors had rubber-mounted their engines as far back as the late 1890s). The power unit was basically a six-cylinder version of the 3-litre, except for the camshaft drive, by a triple-throw crank and connecting rods rather than the kingshaft.

Sales of the $6\frac{1}{2}$-litre were never over 129 in a year; in the model's first twelve months only 58 were pro-

*Near right:* the 6½-litre Speed-Six engine was basically a 6-cylinder version of the 3-litre, except for the camshaft drive which used a triple-throw crank and connecting rods rather than a kingshaft

*Centre right:* a 1927 Speed-Six, racing in a recent vintage sports car meeting. As with all the Bentleys, this model came with many different body styles, depending on customer preference

*Below right:* a Bentley 4½-litre Maythorne, built by Weymann. Over 500 4½-litres, in various guises, were built between 1927 and 1930. Weymann bodies were evident on many cars of the period and were easily recognised

duced. By that time the big Bentley was available in three wheelbase lengths—11 ft, 12 ft 1¼ in, 12 ft 7¼ in—'it was possible to fit anything from a two-seater to a hearse body with complete comfort', recalled W.O.

The launching of the 6½-litre coincided with a series of financial crises caused by the new car's escalating development costs, and it was only a massive injection of cash by the wealthy Bentley *aficionado*, Woolf Barnato, which saved the company from disaster.

Though the 3-litre had been Bentley's most successful model, and was available in several forms including a short-chassis 100 mph version, W.O. now decided it was played out. As the 6½-litre had been intended as a town car, a new four needed to be developed, to give enthusiasts the 'bloody thump' that the six lacked.

So once again the company scattered its fire when the financial situation dictated that they did the exact opposite. In 1926 work started on a 4½-litre four—the Big Six less two cylinders—which was announced the following year, early enough for one of the first models to compete at Le Mans. There it was eliminated 5½ hours after the start in a multiple pileup, at White House corner, which also involved the other two works cars—both 3-litres—and two French cars. The story of how Sammy Davis and Dudley Benjafield managed to beat the crack French teams with the only 3-litre capable of running after the accident—though badly damaged—has passed into motoring's folklore; the episode also proved that the 3-litre was still competitive.

Indeed, in the 1928 Le Mans, the team of three 4½-litres was all but eliminated by chassis weakness; Clement retired and Barnato's winning car covered the last lap with a broken frame and no water in the radiator, while Tim Birkin had crashed early on and lost too much time to stand a chance.

The Bentley swansong came in 1929—for the first time, the company was showing a profit, mostly due to the modest sales of the 6½-litre, now available in sporting Speed Six guise—and the works team had their best-ever season, culminating in an impressive 1-2-3-4 victory at Le Mans, with Barnato's Speed Six leading three 4½-litres home. But the seeds of disaster, sewn by Bentley's undisciplined marketing tactics—another model, the 8-litre six, was already on the stocks—were beginning to sprout: though production of 3-litres had ended in 1929, the 4½-litre failed to come anywhere near its sales figures and output of this model tailed away from the start.

The need to build 50 supercharged 4½-litres—a 'go-faster' version devised by Sir Henry Birkin—was, according to W.O., a 'perversion' of the model's *raison d'être*; but he built the Blower Bentleys all the same, when the company's delicate finances should have persuaded him to refuse to have anything to do with it.

The worldwide slump had, judging by the sales figures, less effect on the company than is often

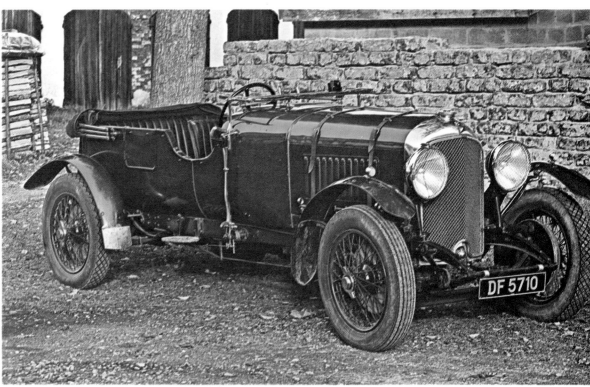

claimed, for 1929 and 1930 were outstanding years for the 6½-litre, with sales of 129 and 126, while 4½-litre output in the period was 260 and 138.

But the firm was rapidly running out of money and Barnato had lost interest, even after his spectacular victory in the 1930 Le Mans, when he beat Rudy Caracciola's Mercedes with a Speed Six, marking the last appearance of a Bentley works racing team.

The new 8-litre, which replaced the 6½-litre at the end of 1930, was probably Bentley's most successful model, but it arrived too late. And the stop-gap 4-litre, introduced at the demand of the Bentley Motors Board to combat the Rolls-Royce 20/25, was a flop which just absorbed much-needed capital.

The blow fell on 11 July 1931, when it was announced that the London Life Assurance Company had applied for a receiver for Bentley Motors, as Barnato had refused to meet mortgages totalling £65,000. Total output of Bentleys was 3051—ten more were to be built after 1931 from spares.

For a while it seemed certain that the company would be taken over by Napier Motors, who were considering re-entry into the luxury car market, and W. O. Bentley even went as far as designing a 6¼-litre Napier-Bentley six—basically a lightened, refined 8-litre—but when the time came for the receiver to apply to the Court for approval of the Napier contract, Rolls-Royce stepped in with some high-power horse-trading and acquired Bentley, lock, stock and W.O.,

*Top:* in 1926 work started on a 4½-litre car whose engine reverted to the earlier four-cylinder form, but with the modifications of the six. The following year, a similar car competed at Le Mans, but was eliminated after the start in a multiple pile-up

*Bottom:* in 1928, Barnato and Rubin drove a 4½-litre to victory at Le Mans. The winning car covered the last lap with a broken frame and a dry radiator

A cutaway of the most
famous Bentley of them·
all—the supercharged
$4\frac{1}{2}$-litre 'Black label'—
which developed 240 bhp
at 2400 rpm in Le Mans
racing trim. The Amherst-
Villiers supercharger was
mounted between the
dumb-irons in front of the
radiator and was driven
direct from the front of
the crankshaft

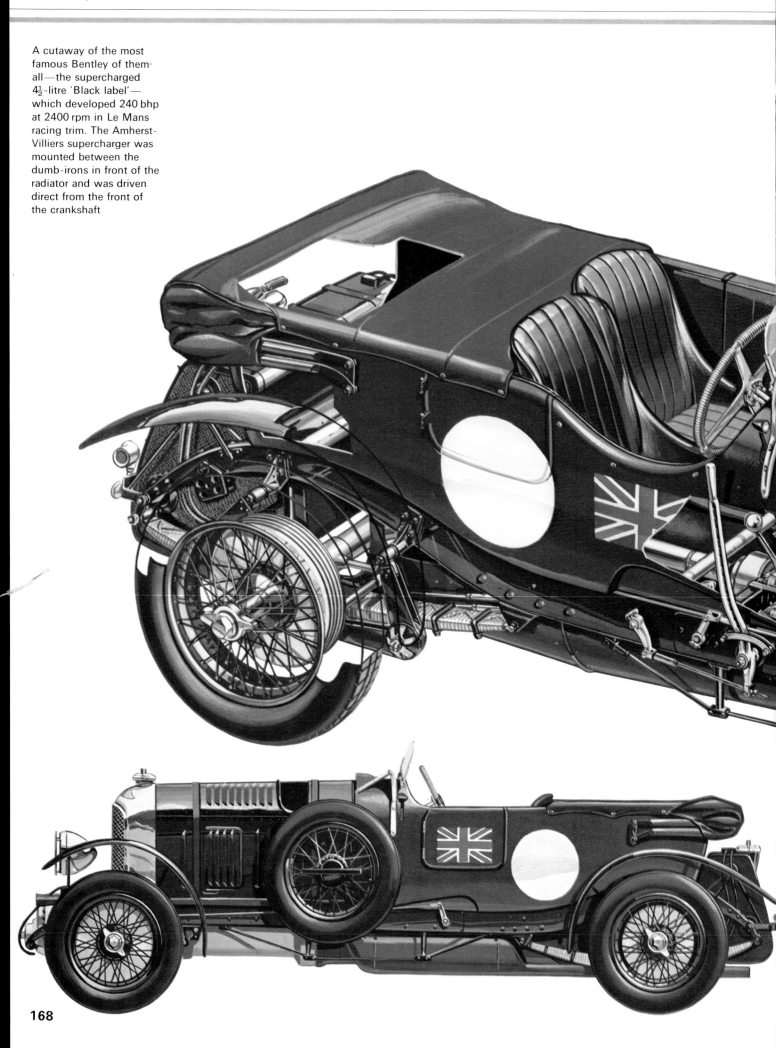

QUATTRORUOTE
COPYRIGHT

at the very last minute. For a time he helped with the development of the $3\frac{1}{2}$-litre Rolls-Bentley, a mildly tuned version of the 20/25 the Bentley 4-litre had been intended to beat, but his heart wasn't in it and as soon as his service contract expired in 1935 he resigned, joining Lagonda of Staines, which had recently been saved from liquidation (and a Rolls-Royce takeover) by a wealthy solicitor named Alan Good.

Given a free hand, Bentley first refined the existing $4\frac{1}{2}$-litre Lagonda six, then, in the space of eighteen months, designed a sophisticated $4\frac{1}{2}$-litre V12, with torsion bar front independent suspension, capable of putting over 100 miles into an hour; it was this model which gave Bentley his last Le Mans success, third and fourth places achieved after a steadily unspectacular drive at a predetermined average of 83 mph.

After the war, Lagonda decided that the V12 was designed for too limited a market, so Bentley designed a new $2\frac{1}{2}$-litre machine for a wider clientele. It was to have been sold as the 'Lagonda-Bentley', but Rolls-Royce stepped in to prevent the use of the Bentley name, and the postwar Labour government refused to allocate steel for more than 100 cars, thus stifling this new design before production had even begun.

The Lagonda company was put up for sale and passed into the ownership of the David Brown organisation. Before the sale, Bentley had been working on two advanced, but still-born, projects, a radial-five-cylinder-engined, 1360 cc model and an air-cooled flat-six with torsion bar suspension.

After the takeover, W. O. Bentley established a consultancy; among the projects he was involved in was an air-cooled flat-four, which was tested in a Morris Minor, and a 3-litre car—an enlarged version of the $2\frac{1}{2}$-litre Lagonda—for Armstrong Siddeley. The latter model was shelved on grounds of excessive cost, the Sapphire being introduced instead.

After this, W.O. was content to retire, retaining only his connection with the Bentley Drivers' Club: he died in 1971.                                    DBW

*Below:* the 1935 Pacey-Hassan used Bentley mechanicals and started life as a $4\frac{1}{2}$-litre, although it ended up with a bored-out and super-charged 3-litre under its bonnet. It is still used in hill-climbs today

*Right:* a 4-cylinder, 3-litre Bentley engine. Present day vintage-Bentley owners take great care to maintain their cars in perfect condition

# FATHER OF THE MOTOR CAR

From his humble beginnings, Carl Benz overcame great trials and tribulations to establish himself as the pioneer of the motor car

CARL BENZ, who descended from a line of mayors and blacksmiths, was born in 1844; he was an inventor certainly, but equally a romantic. He is the man most entitled to be called the inventor of the motor car.

Carl's father, who was a railway engine-driver, died when Carl was two, but a devoted mother let her prize engineering student attend Karlsruhe Polytechnic, where he trained under an internal combustion seer. Carl graduated in 1864, three years before Daimler became head engineer there; the two never met.

Benz then did obligatory work as a trainee, at shop-floor wages, for several firms. After his mother's death, he met a girl named Bertha and, thanks to her advance dowry, co-founded a Mannheim engineering firm in 1871. A year later, having split with his partner, he married Bertha, the major influence on his life.

Then disaster struck and they faced bankruptcy in 1877, as Carl was attempting to build his first engine. Since Otto had patented the four-stroke, Benz designed a two-stroke engine, but it refused to run. Bertha insisted they try just once more after New Year's Eve supper 1879. It fired and 'sang' as Benz recalled in his memoirs.

He was, at first, refused a German engine patent, although items basic to all engines, such as his 1882 speed regulator, were protected in Germany and abroad. A dedicated improver, Benz realized flame ignition was dangerous for stationary engines. He worked out a battery system and even built his own spark plugs.

With funds from a court photographer, he opened a gas-engine factory, but found that his partners were chiefly interested in profits. Leaving after three months, Benz found two more backers from his cycle club. He decided that Benz & Co would build engines —one, two and four-horsepower models by 1885— which underwrote his car dreams, already a sore point with the partners.

Benz had turned to four-stroke work in 1884, seeking 'a dwarf in weight, a titan in power' which would be integral to his vehicle; this was his unswerving goal.

A three-wheeler was finished (and driven into the wall during its first test) in late 1885, only months after the engine first ran. Early tests were made without a fuel tank, using petrol in the surface (sponge-type) carburettor.

His original horizontal, water-cooled, cast-iron single produced about two or three horsepower at a then-high 250 rpm. Benz was not satisfied with Model I, nor was he with II, though it had a sort of carburettor float, while III gave only 1.5 hp.

Seeking better ignition, he turned to a flywheel-driven generator and a patent was granted in 1888 for his current regulator. Benz was proud that 'short visits' did not require one to stop the 'absolutely safe' engine. Pulling a belt-control arm back from drive to the mid-point gave 'neutral'. Another notch to the

*Above right:* the world's first motor car? The first Benz was a three-wheeler with tiller steering and chain drive and made its debut in 1885. It featured a water-cooled, cast-iron, single-cylinder engine which developed 0.9 hp at 500 rpm. The machine had a top speed of 9 mph

*Above left:* a later version of the three-wheeler Benz. This model, built in 1888, developed 1.5 bhp and had an increased top speed— 10 mph

rear brought brakes of a sort into action. To Carl, a car was not usable unless capable of negotiating any road, so he designed a differential too.

The initial Benz had a steel-tube frame, elliptic rear springs and 'engine access'. Wheelbase was 57·1 in, weight 585 lb. Unable to solve car steering, Benz used a single front wheel, moved by a cog and twin racks.

The press was largely favourable, though the German Yearbook of Natural Science for 1888 dismissed the Benz as an idea with no future. Bertha and their two oldest sons had already proved otherwise.

Leaving papa asleep at home, they left Mannheim at 5 am one August morning to become the first cross-country motor-car travellers. The trio bought apothecary petrol, had a cobbler replace brake block facings, asked an innkeeper for the way around one mountain and pushed up another hill—to reach Pforzheim, near Stuttgart, after dark.

Carl didn't scold them, but he did insist on them returning the drive chain necessary for his demonstration car at the Munich technical exhibition. He had permission for drives around town between 2 and 4 pm, giving rides to the daring, provided that the police heard no complaints.

At home the Duchy of Baden had banned self-propelled road vehicles in 1887—the year one friend

*Below right:* a Benz 8 hp 'Break' of 1889

*Below left:* an early steering wheel

*Bottom left:* the highly successful Benz Velo

first put a Benz engine in his boat. Not until 1893 was Benz allowed on the highways: at 7 mph on open, straight roads, or 3½ mph in towns and on corners (thus Bertha was not only the first lady driver, but also the first illegal one). Such bans hardly boosted sales. It was 1895 before Benz could legally move any faster.

Following acclaim and a gold medal at the Munich

exhibition, plus an illustrated story in a Leipzig paper, the company expected to sell many cars, but customers were still rare. One father cancelled his son's order on the grounds that the boy had been acting crazily lately. Benz' partners withdrew at this point, but, once again, he carried on regardless.

He also developed, after two years' work, a three-piece front axle with steering knuckles; this work culminated in an 1893 patent. 1893 was also the year in which the company sold 500 stationary engines, which brought in substantial income.

The first four-wheeler Benz car was called a Victoria and was strictly a 'horseless carriage'. One of these cars was proven in 1894 by von Liebig, a Bohemian textile magnate, who drove his to Rheims. During the first 450 of the 750 miles, covered in 57 hours, he used 310 lb of fuel and 330 gallons of water.

This 1543 lb car had a 2.9-litre, one-cylinder engine developing 3 hp at 400 rpm. Sold as a two-seater for 3800 marks, it was available with extras too: a small third seat or a 4–5 hp engine.

Benz' master stroke, however, was scaling the Victoria down to become the Velo. This soon made him the most successful motor-car producer of his age.

*Above:* even in 1910, Benz cars resembled the coaches of earlier times. This model used a four-cylinder engine developing 40 bhp. It can be seen in a Portuguese motor museum

*Left:* by 1914, the Benz company had come a long way from the original cyclecars of the 19th century. This four-seater open tourer used a two-litre, four-cylinder engine

*Top left:* a 1921 6/18 PS

*Centre left:* the 1910 Blitzen Benz

*Bottom left:* this streamlined Blitzen Benz, driven by Bob Burman, achieved a top speed of 140 mph at Daytona

*Below right:* another of Burman's Blitzen racing cars. These cars gained great success

*Bottom right:* the 4-cylinder, 21-litre Blitzen Benz engine

In 1895, the company built 135 vehicles, 62 of them Velos. France bought 49 cars and a Benz won the first American 'race', albeit by default.

This 2000-mark Velo appeared with 1.5 and later 2 and 3/4 hp engines and two gears (third gear and pneumatic tyres being optional), but power soon grew. Very light at 615 lb, the Velo encouraged the gentle sport of motoring which Benz had always wanted. Growth was satisfying at first: in 1898 Benz sold 434 cars and by the end of 1899 the company had delivered over 2000.

There were several models: the up-to-6 hp Phaeton with four seats in two rows or a Vis à Vis (face to face) with a front bench facing the driver. By 1899 the latter had side doors and did 17 mph.

The first Benz twin had two singles side by side, but Carl soon designed his smoother opposed twin. This powered cars like the Dos à Dos (back to back), offering 5–10 hp at 750 rpm, with high-tension igni-tion, single carburettor and 25 mph top speed.

Around 1900, he also built panel vans, 'overland' buses and proper trucks. The Benz name was known by now from London to St Petersburg, from Buenos Aires to Singapore and down to Cape Town.

Yet Carl wasn't happy. Racing was becoming important to car manufacturers and the company had only a French importer, Emile Roger, to carry the Benz banner, odd entries apart. 1900 was the best year of all for Benz, with 603 deliveries, but the firm sold only 385 vehicles in 1901, while directors Benz and Julius Ganss clashed regularly.

Ganss ignored the founder to order a vertical twin from their design office. Finished late in 1902, this fell short of Benz standards, so Ganss hired Marius Barbarou to build-up his own staff in France and produce a range of cars—including a racer.

Carl was bitterly opposed to 'strangers' in his domain. He backed the original German design office in direct confrontation. The French finished their car first, but it was faulty so they quit in 1904.

By then, Benz himself had withdrawn from the firm, only returning as a director when Ganss left in 1904. Meanwhile, designs had been pooled to build a new car, to be known as the Parsifal. This was a radical departure with two upright cylinders cast as a pair up front, with shaft drive to the rear. A four-cylinder Parsifal racer gave as much as 60 hp.

Well before 1908, when a 120 hp Benz (forerunner of the Blitzen) took second place to a Daimler in the French GP, the firm of C. Benz & Sons was well established in nearby romantic Ladenburg. Carl's sons, Eugen and Richard, joined their father and finally took over the company in 1912.

The original firm began to co-operate with Daimler and this led to a merger in 1925, with Carl taking a seat on the Daimler-Benz board. Although Daimler-Benz now tends to favour Gottlieb Daimler, Carl Benz outlived his rival pioneer by nearly three decades and saw the automobile become an everyday sight.

Carl died on 4 April 1929 at the age of 85, but Bertha lived another fifteen years, dying at 95.    JS

# GIVING BEAUTY TO THE BEAST

Giovanni Bertone is one of the world's most respected coachbuilders. His creations are individual and exciting and they embody the glamour and style that is typically Italian

*Below:* the SPA 9000 sport of 1921 was the very first car Giovanni Bertone turned his hand to. It was very popular and Bertone received many orders

*Bottom:* another of Bertone's early designs, based on the Fiat 501 chassis. This model was first produced in 1923

GIOVANNI BERTONE was born in Mondovi during 1884, and it was here that he took his first steps in the coach-building world, in a carriage and wagon repair shop. He moved to Turin in 1907, by which time the city was already an industrial centre, and he spent five years in the workshops of the Diatto company, making railway rolling stock. In 1912, he decided to become his own master, so he set up a carriage repairing and building company in Turin.

Giovanni Bertone's first official encounter with the motor car took place in 1921, when he was offered the opportunity of building a body for a SPA 9000 sport. One chassis followed another, as did the orders, and soon he gave up carriage building. For many years he worked for Lancia and SPA, but without putting his name to his work—the bodywork being regarded as that of the chassis manufacturer. Indeed, much the same could be said of some of his work as recently as

the 60s, when the Bertone works were turning out Lancia Flaminias with the Pininfarina badge, indicating the organization responsible for the design if not for the construction.

In the end, his modest sheds in Turin's via Villarbasse proved inadequate, so he moved to extensive new works, still in Turin. This eased his problems in dealing with Lancia orders, for the Lancia works were in the same street. Based on an agreement with Vincenzo Lancia, Bertone undertook small series production of Lancia body shells, reaching the impressive total, over the years, of 3000 units.

In 1934, a further stage in the life of the organization began. Giovanni Bertone was beginning to find difficulty in obtaining chassis from the manufacturers and, for some time, had been producing so-called 'one-off' bodies for private orders. Thus, in 1934, the works moved to another address in Turin and, in the same year, Giovanni Bertone's twenty-year-old son, Giuseppe, nicknamed Nuccio, joined the company.

There was a third, no less significant, development in the same year. For the first time, Carrozzeria Bertone offered an example of its products for public appraisal, by exhibiting a special-bodied Fiat Ardita six-cylinder, the Superaerodinamica, at the Milan Motor Show. A saloon, with a three-person bench front seat on tubular framing, this car had a number of unusual features. The windscreen was continued round the sides of the body and into the roof, and the spare wheel was located beneath the wide bonnet which also incorporated the headlights.

In the years before World War II, the number of Bertone special bodies increased progressively. Especially worthy of mention is the series of coupés, which was not only typical of its period, in the sense that all the models resembled the styling of other coachbuilders, but also built with exceptional skill. A particularly good example is the open-tourer body, designed and built for the Alfa Romeo 6C 2300B chassis, a very smooth design, with a retractable rear windscreen, an unusual feature in Italian coachbuilding of the time. Moreover, Bertone revealed his skill in achieving such good results while retaining the standard Alfa Romeo radiator grille, headlights and bumpers.

When work restarted after the war, the factory employed 150 people. Once again, Bertone was working for one of the major manufacturers with the Fiat 1100 Derby in spider and coupé forms. This time, however, these small series-production models carried a badge with the letter 'b'. Also produced in small series or as unique examples were a number of special bodied Fiat 1400s, as well as the first Lancia Aurelias, but these bodies carried a 'Bertone' badge. Also dating from this period were a few Borgward and Ferrari bodies.

On 7 September 1952, at the Elkhart Lake (Wisconsin) sports-car races, S. H. Arnolt of Chicago presented

*Above:* the Carabo, based on the Alfa Romeo 33

*Right:* the 1954 Alfa-Romeo Guilietta sprint

*Below:* Bertone's version of the 1936 Fiat 508

*Bottom:* the 1934 Superaerodinamica. The windscreen continued into the roof

two Bertone-bodied MG TDs, one a convertible and the other a hard top coupé, but both offered at 3585 dollars. This was the first sign of the eventual direction the company was to take.

Thus began the first major export effort, while Bertone continued to produce new designs which appeared regularly at the various motor shows. At the Paris Show in 1952, an Abarth coupé with aero-dynamic lines was displayed, distinguished by its three headlamps and by the styling accent placed on the side panels, along which the wheel arch shape was continued. A Lancia Aurelia was also exhibited. At the Turin Show in 1953, Bertone showed the fifth version of the famous 'BAT', the 'Berlinetta Aerodinamica Tecnica', on an Alfa Romeo 1900 Sprint chassis, with steeply inclined windscreen and large rear fins. Another design of the same period was the Siata 208S V8 which resembled, on a small scale, the Ferraris of the period.

In addition to producing the Bertone MGs for the United States, production began of a 2-litre Arnolt-Bristol type 404, with its steel body welded to a suitably shortened chassis.

At the 1954 Turin Show, Bertone exhibited the Storm Z 250 on a modified Dodge chassis, evidently devised to suit American tastes. He also showed the BAT 7, which, like the earlier versions, was designed by Franco Scaglione on the Alfa Romeo 1900 Sprint chassis. It still incorporated the retractable headlamps, although it used a different system, but it had enlarged fins and a lower nose. That year, however, by far the most important coachbuilding exhibit was the sleek, light blue coupé on show on the Alfa Romeo stand. The catalogues described it as 'sporting, aerodynamic, nimble, fast and modern'. The strikingly new Giulietta Sprint was the first of a long series, even though the prototype at the 1954 Turin Show, with its opening rear window providing access to the luggage compartment, did not carry the inimitable 'b' badge.

When the Bertone works re-opened in 1945, each of the new designs was numbered starting from zero. The Giulietta Sprint coupé design, which was to mark a

decisive leap forward in the company's history, was design number 37. In the thirteen years that followed, Bertone produced over 40,000 examples.

This scale of production necessitated a new move. In 1951, a new factory at Grugliasco was officially inaugurated and opened up new horizons. In 1960, alone, Bertone produced some 31,000 bodies, ranging from the Fiat 850 Spider to the Fiat Dino and Simca 1200S coupés, as well as the Alfa Romeo Montreal and various Lamborghinis.

The number of designs increased progressively: the 100 figure was reached with the building of a special Ford Mustang, commissioned by the American magazine, *Automobile Quarterly*. It was exhibited at the New York International Show of 1965. In all, it had taken twenty years to reach this number of projects, but it took only seven more years, up to the Turin Show of November 1972, to add another 500 designs, the Lancia Fulvia Stratos HF actually being project number 600.

The company remained faithful to its established policy. This was indicated when the Fiat 850 Spider was launched. 'Our role is the production of car body-work on which we impose the styling trends, build prototypes, develop the design, the production methods and the tooling. Naturally we produce them in quantity.' Carrozzeria Bertone of G. Bertone & Company continued to dedicate its policy to special vehicles: to unique bodies as much as to the series production of special versions. The inexhaustible creativity revealed by the 600 projects, laid down and built since 1945, is so large that only a restricted number of designs can be discussed. Among those unveiled before the development of the Ford Mustang project, mention should be made of the attractive Arnolt-

*Right, clockwise:* 1961 Ferrari 250 GT
1970 Lancia Stratos
1972 Lamborghini Countach
1968 Alfa Romeo Carabo
1958 Jaguar XK 140
1971 Lancia, Ferrari-Dino-engined, HF Stratos

*Left, top to bottom:*
1958 NSU Prinz coupé
1966 mid-engined Lamborghini Miura
1967 Fiat Dino coupé
1964 Alfa Romeo 1600 Giulia
1970 BMW Garmish which inspired BMW to design the 520 and 525 range

Bristol coupé, the slightly futuristic design with which, in 1955, the series of cars built for S. H. Arnolt came to an end.

Altogether, some 500 cars were built on MG and Bristol chassis. Other notable designs included the extremely low Abarth 215A, with retractable headlights, shown at Geneva in 1956, the Alfa Romeo Sportiva and the first Veloce versions of the Giulietta Sprint which, while retaining the basic parameters of the standard version, were both lighter and faster as a result of using aluminium for the bonnet, doors and boot lid and Plexiglass for the side and rear windows.

At Turin, in 1957, Bertone showed an outstanding Aston Martin, and an American magazine voted the new Giulietta Sprint Special 'Car of the Year'. At the Paris show of 1958, Bertone exhibited the prototype NSU Sport Prinz. In July 1961, having already pro-

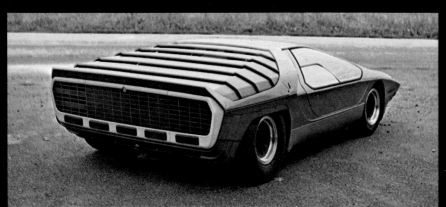

*Above and left:* the 1967 Lamborghini Marzal featured a mid-mounted, 6-cylinder, 2-litre engine producing 175 bhp. The engine was essentially half a V12 Miura. The car also featured a six-headlamp system, transparent gull-wing doors and a transparent roof

duced the first 20,000 Giulietta Sprints, the company introduced a two-plus-two coupé version of the Alfa Romeo 2000 Sprint to that company's order. Outstanding new designs were the Aston Martin DB4 Jet (Geneva 1961), which was noteworthy because of the use of light alloy, and the 250 GT Ferrari coupé (Turin the same year), in which the roof and the internal body panels were made of stainless steel and the headlamps were concealed behind a metal grille. These were followed by the BMW 3200 CS coupé, the ASA 1000, the prototype Iso Rivolta Grifo and, subsequently, its 'road' version, while the appearance of a saloon design for the Japanese Toyo Kogyo company indicated how international Bertone's work had become.

The most interesting development of the early 60s was the Testudo shown at the Geneva Show in 1963. Based on the Chevrolet Corvair Monza, this was a grand-touring car design study which stood only 42 inches high—$5\frac{1}{2}$ inches less than the little ASA coupé—and revealed such details as a built-in roll-over bar, completely retractable headlights, side lamps of polycarbonate material recessed in the bumpers, and the front, so that it lifted to give access to the interior. glass, the upper part being tinted in blue and hinged at the front so that it lifted to give access to the interior. At the Paris Show, in 1964, Bertone exhibited the

Canguro, based on the Alfa Romeo Giulia 1600 Tubolare, with an outline possibly even more slender than the Testudo. A feature of this model was the bonding of the screens to the metal pillars, a procedure hitherto exclusively employed in the aircraft industry. At the 1965 Geneva Show, Bertone showed the Fiat 850 Spider, a design of great originality with the headlights steeply inclined to blend into the line of the bonnet, taking something from the Testudo design.

Among the 500 designs carried out between 1965 and 1972, there are some which were extremely significant. First among these without doubt is the legendary Lamborghini P400 Miura, shown at Geneva in 1966, the superbly sleek, individual line of this model revealing the influence of wind tunnel studies. A unique car, as original in its internal layout as in its external appearance, it is a creation as different from the Superaerodinamica 900 of 1934, with which Bertone first appealed to public interest, as anything could be.

After the Miura came the Carabo at the 1968 Paris Show, another 'bravura' effort built on an Alfa Romeo type 33 chassis, a striking wedge-shaped design, which had front-hinged gull-wing doors. At Geneva the following year, the company showed the BMW Spicub with a retractable metal roof replacing the canvas top. At the same show the following year, the Alfa Romeo Montreal appeared, while at Turin 1971, the Lancia Fulvia HF Stratos was shown in prototype form.

It would be difficult, if not impossible, to establish a common denominator or even to identify a common thread among these 600 designs, all dating from the end of World War II. A prototype is conceived with an altogether different spirit from that for a series production car, even a special-bodied one. The coachbuilder, even more than having to adhere to a personal style, must also provide an inexhaustible source of ideas and must be guided in his work, not only by good taste, but also by production feasibility.

From the 1921 SPA, through the anonymous body shells built for Lancia, Ceirano and Diatto, and the many modest versions of the Fiat Balilla, Carrozzeria Bertone has graduated to the Ferrari, Lamborghini and Maserati levels. Through their hands have passed American, French, English, German, as well as Italian chassis and they have also built thousands of bodies which, despite their numbers, were in every case, individual. If the Pininfarina studios were responsible for establishing the 'Italian Line' in the world, making Turin the indisputable centre of motor-car styling, it is to coachbuilders like Bertone that the merit of having maintained this prestige has passed.                ERH

# UNSPECTACULAR BUT SUCCESSFUL

Bianchi won no racing fame, established no world records and built no epoch-making models. Their survival was a triumph of moderation and dependability

*Above:* Edoardo Bianchi gained his early reputation from the manufacture of bicycles

*Left:* a very early four-wheeler (1899–1900), which used a de Dion single-cylinder engine

*Bottom:* in 1907, Bianchi was producing several models with interchangeable parts

*Below:* Bianchi used this emblem when the company started in 1885

*Below right:* in 1901, Bianchi four-wheelers were still utilising the de Dion engine

THE AUTOBIANCHI COMPANY produces over 200,000 cars a year and is Italy's third biggest car manufacturer. Yet, this all seems very far away from the humble beginnings, back in 1855, of the Bianchi company, from which they have derived their name.

Edoardo Bianchi, the son of the proprietor of a large grocery firm, opened his own Milan workshop at the age of twenty, in 1885, and started to manufacture bicycles of the English pattern, which were an immediate success. By 1890, he had acquired an established reputation for his products which were well known for successes in road and track races in Italy and abroad.

It was not until 1897 that Edoardo turned his attention to motor cycles and, in the following year, to producing his first four-wheeler. It was based on bicycle techniques, with a steel-tube frame and a single-cylinder, air-cooled de Dion engine powering the rear wheels. By 1900, the Bianchi works in Milan had grown to a substantial size and were devoted almost entirely to motor-cycle and bicycle production. Clearly, development work on the original quadri-cycle had continued, because in 1900 a second single-cylinder

car was produced, again using the 942 cc de Dion unit driving the rear wheels by chain. At this point, the Bianchi company took a decisive step in the direction of motor car manufacture: an engineer, Giuseppe Merosi, joined the company to develop the motor car side of production.

A range of increasingly powerful and fast touring cars was evolved: by 1907 a new factory was producing three chassis types of different wheelbase lengths, all using interchangeable components. The engines were of the four-cylinder, side-valve type, driving the rear wheels through a four-speed gearbox and a chain. Another personality who was to play a considerable part in the future of the company now joined Edoardo Bianchi—Gian Fernando Tommaselli. The scale of production was increased even further and an ultra-modern plant was built, from which Bianchi cars were produced for the Italian and world markets until World War II. Despite the fact that at this stage the company had not applied the principles of line production to its

Coupé da città a otto molle sopra chassis 15-20 HP

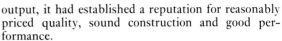

output, it had established a reputation for reasonably priced quality, sound construction and good performance.

New for 1908 was the type G, which featured a modern, L-head, monobloc, four-cylinder engine and, initially, a three-speed gearbox (by 1910 it had acquired a further ratio). An interesting development, for an Italian manufacturer, was the type S of 1914, an inexpensive 1244 cc three-speed car, available in only one body style and one colour. Electrics were an optional extra, but were standard on Bianchi's wartime newcomer the 3.3-litre B-type of 1915. The S was enlarged to 1460 cc in 1916, but disappeared shortly after World War I in favour of the type 12.

Vintage Bianchis typified the more conservative strain in Italian design, with little sporting flavour, although they did build a contender for a 2-litre Grand

*Above:* ideal for the chauffeur-driven rich, the 20/30 landaulette of 1910 used a four-cylinder, in-line engine

*Above left:* the type S was announced in 1914 with only one body style and one colour

*Below left:* the type A, of 1913, was the smallest of the range. It featured a four-cylinder, 2120 cc engine and was supposed to compete with the Fiat type O

*Below:* introduced and shown here at the 1920 Brussels Motor Show, the type 15 used an engine of 1692 cc

Prix in 1922. The car had a dohc four-cylinder engine and produced over 90 bhp. Unfortunately the project was shelved. In 1923, a new model, the type 16, was produced to replace the 12, and it featured a detachable cylinder head. The firm also brought out, at the same time, the 2-litre, pushrod type 18, which was very popular with English coachbuilders of the period.

It was not until 1924, with the arrival of Antonio Santoni to the company as chief engineer, that the company turned to the small car sector of the market, with the S4. Like the larger, 2300 cc type 20 which was produced at the same time, the S4 retained one distinguishing feature, that of a separate gearbox driven by a short shaft from the clutch and driving the rear wheels via another short shaft.

Santoni's S4, which was Bianchi's answer to the Fiat 509, developed year by year, via the S5 of 1927, until it was replaced, in 1935, by the 1452 cc S9, which remained in production until 1939. It featured a five-

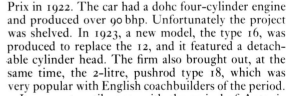

1931 saw the introduction of the S8, which was powered by a new 2.9-litre straight eight. This engine, which produced 85 bhp at 4000 rpm, used pushrod-operated overhead valves for the first time. Several body styles were available, among them the one shown here, which was a lightweight touring car. This was a false convertible, the roof being fixed, although it looked removable

*Below left:* the S4 was Bianchi's answer to the Fiat 509; it marked the company's entry into the small-car field in 1924. The car shown here was a taxi version

*Below:* the S5 superseded the S4, but was not very different in design. This is the 'torpedo' of 1927

*Above:* the S5 'Viareggio' of 1932. This was only one of the many body styles available

*Right:* a batch of S5 'torpedos' specially prepared for the highway police and the Customs and Excise department

*Below:* the S9 saloon of 1935. Featuring a four-cylinder, 1452 cc engine, this was the last of the Bianchi line

bearing crankshaft and, by 1936, had acquired hydraulic brakes and a synchromesh gearbox, though, unusually for a cheap Italian car, it rode on beam axles all round and wore Rudge type wire wheels. Also made was a long-wheelbase six/seven-seater version of the S9 which was used as a taxicab.

During World War II, the Bianchi works were turned over to the production of heavy commercial vehicles, most of them with diesel engines. Towards the end of 1943, the Milan factory was almost completely destroyed by bombing, but production continued in other premises. In 1946, Edoardo Bianchi died, aged 81, his principal collaborator Tommaselli having died a few years earlier. After this, car production ceased, lorries being responsible for the company's survival until 1955 when, with Fiat and Pirelli backing, the company was given a new lease of life under the name of Autobianchi.

*Above right:* the series 2 cabriolet version of the S9 had neat, flowing lines. It featured hydraulic brakes

*Right:* by 1936, the straight four, which powered the S9, had acquired a 5-bearing crankshaft. Power output was 42 bhp at 4000 rpm

Although it may seem rather uncharitable to say so, perhaps the most outstanding achievement of the Bianchi company is that it has survived, in a form, to this day. It can trace its origins back to 1885 and yet in the intervening years, unlike most Italian car manufacturers, has won no racing fame, established no world records and built no epoch-making models. Despite such apparent handicaps the Bianchi achieved a very respectable position in the world car manufacturers' league on a basis of honest, unspectacular, dependable family cars, a kind of middle-class respectability, which gives a firm the ability to survive.     AW

# The Grand Prix Prince

Bira won the first London Grand Prix, at Crystal Palace in 1937, driving an ERA. Charles Follett presented the cup to him. In the background is Bira's cousin, Chula

ONLY A COUPLE of generations after the redoubtable Mrs Anna Leonowens had turned the Siamese Court upside down (which inspired the musical, *The King and I*), the English influence was still strong. So it was natural that the King's nephews, the three young Siamese Princes, Abhas, Birabongse and Chirasakti, should come to England in the 1920s for their education. Birabongse, the second oldest (he was born in 1914), had been crazy about cars ever since, as a little boy, he had sat on the lap of a chauffeur and steered one of the royal cars.

He didn't get the chance to drive on the roads, however, until he was sixteen at Eton; his elder cousin and guardian, Chula, allowed Bira, as he was known, to drive his 1928, 12 hp, sleeve-valve Voisin—'a wonderful little machine'.

In 1932, Chula presented Bira with an MG Magna, soon replaced by a 4½-litre Super Sports Invicta, which itself was succeeded by a 3½-litre Rolls-Bentley in June 1934. The cousins were keen fans of motor racing, but Chula refused to let Bira compete in speed events. However, he bought him a Riley Imp for reliability trials; in 1935 Bira managed to get Chula's permission to turn the Imp into a racing car, and it was taken to Thomson & Taylor at Brooklands for tuning.

For their racing livery, the cousins used a light blue based on the colour of an evening frock belonging to a young Danish girl, Barbara Grut: this later became the Siamese national racing colour (yellow was added to it in 1939).

Birabongse decided to adopt the *nom de course* of 'B. Bira' and first appeared at Brooklands at the opening meeting of the 1935 season; but the Imp proved too slow, and Bira looked around for a new car. Cecil Kimber of MG offered him the very last supercharged MG Magnette ever built, which had been specially prepared for the Mille Miglia but refused entry papers for Italy. The MG gave Bira much valuable racing experience, but its top speed of around 110 mph was not quite fast enough to put him in the prize money, though it enabled him to establish a reputation as a driver of consistent ability—and his distinctive Siamese pit signals caused a great deal of attention.

The new ERA cars were just beginning to enjoy their first international racing success, so Chula decided to buy a 1500 cc ERA as a present for Bira's 21st birthday, which fell on 15 July 1935. Five days later, Bira took second place in the 1500 cc race at Dieppe, beating such polished drivers as Earl Howe (Delage), Raymond Mays, Dick Seaman and Humphrey Cook (ERA) and Veyron (Bugatti); only an oiled plug prevented him from taking first place.

This success inspired Bira to enter the 1500 cc Swiss Grand Prix at Berne; again he came second after a well driven race, this time beaten by Dick Seaman. However, a drive for Aston Martin in the Ulster TT ended in failure when an oil pipe broke on the second lap.

Nevertheless, a few days later, Bira set up a new Mountain Circuit lap record at Brooklands with the ERA and then achieved fifth place in the Donington GP, the highest position taken by a 1½-litre car in this race. He wound up his first season by setting up fastest time at the Gatwick Speed Trials in the ERA, then, at the other end of the speed cycle, won a gold medal in the Veteran Car Run at the tiller of a 1903 Oldsmobile.

In 1936, Bira added to his stable, buying a 2.9-litre 8CM Maserati, with which he won the British Empire Trophy at Brooklands; two of the 1927 1½-litre Delages (which were still capable of winning races in the hands of Dick Seaman) were subsequent additions. They were fitted with ugly streamlined bodies and independent front suspension, but these modifications seemed to break the winning streak.

Bira drove a wide variety of cars, but achieved his most notable victories with ERA—he eventually had three of them—Romulus and Remus, both B-types, and the C-type Hanuman, named after the Siamese monkey-god.

Most successful was his 21st birthday present, Romulus, which took ten first places, eight seconds, five thirds, one fourth and one fifth in the 1935 to 1939 seasons, only retiring five times.

Bira returned to racing in 1946 with Romulus and Hanuman (which had been rebuilt as a B-type after a crash in 1939) and won the Ulster TT. In the 1947 Pau Grand Prix, Romulus's engine disintegrated in full view of 20,000 spectators.

Bira had by now bought a new 4CL Maserati, but on its first outing, in the 1947 Junior Car Club race in Jersey, the engine seized solid and Bira returned to the pits on a borrowed bicycle. His old 2.9 Maserati failed him in practice for the 1947 Grand Prix des Frontieres at Chimay, so he substituted the 1½-litre car and finished an easy winner, despite trouble with failing oil pressure.

Later in 1947, Bira had his first works drive for the Simca-Gordini team, winning the Coupe des Petites Cylindrées at Reims. He then had an easy victory in the Manx Cup Race, came second in the Prix de Lyons and, in the Prix de Leman at Lausanne, he narrowly beat his team mate Sommer.

The 1948 season saw a third at Jersey and a win at Zandvoort, both in 1½-litre Maseratis (the latter victory in one of the new 4CLT/48 cars), and at the end of the year his partnership with Chula was dissolved.

In 1949, Bira continued racing his new Maserati, winning the Swedish GP, coming second in the Argentine Mar del Plata GP, the GP de Roussillon at Perpignan, the Albi GP and the GP of the Associated French Motor Clubs, and taking third places at Zandvoort and in the GPs of Europe and Italy.

In 1950, Bira had an unsuccessful season with the Maserati, gaining only a first and a fourth, and the transplant of a V12, 4.5-litre Osca engine into the Maserati brought little better fortune in 1951. Bira returned to Siam in 1952–3, but was back on the circuits in 1954 with a new 250F Maserati, gaining one first, two seconds and a fourth; the next year he won the New Zealand Grand Prix and came third in the Silverstone International Trophy, but decided to retire permanently from racing and sold the Maserati.

Bira returned to his native Thailand to run an airline. DBW

185

# Blower Bentleys and Bravado

Birkin's single-seater 4½-litre Blower Bentley

TO A GENERATION of motor-racing enthusiasts, Sir Henry R. S. (Tim) Birkin was the epitome of the glamour of motor racing, the fearless driver at the wheel of a great green Bentley, blue-and-white spotted silk scarf a-flutter at his throat.

Yet he was small of stature, stuttered badly and his driving could mechanically wreck a car faster and more completely than any other top racing motorist of the late 1920s.

Birkin was born into a wealthy Nottingham family in 1896, and turned to motor racing in 1921 as a relief from the boredom of post-war office work. His first competition car was a DFP, which he raced at Brooklands, achieving no better than a second place in a minor event. After his first few races, business reasons compelled him to give up racing for several years and he did not appear in serious competition again until 1927, when he and his brother Archie—killed a month later practising for the motorcycle TT—drove a 3-litre Bentley to third place in the Essex MC Six-Hour race at Brooklands.

The next year, Tim Birkin's 4½-litre Bentley again came third in the Six-Hour race and this made him decide, despite opposition from his father, to make motor racing his profession.

In the 1928 Le Mans, Birkin was partnered by the veteran Jean Chassagne. Their Bentley led for the first 20 laps until a rear tyre burst at 100 mph and the tyre canvas jammed itself steadfastly in the brake mechanism. As the Bentleys, to reduce weight, were not carrying jacks, Birkin had to try and free the wheel with 'a jack-knife, a file, a hammer and some pliers'.

After 90 minutes he had the remains of the tyre off the wheel, and began to drive back to the pits on the rim at 60 mph. At Arnage, three miles from the pits, the wheel disintegrated and the Bentley slid into the ditch. Birkin ran for help and when he arrived at the pits the 47-year-old Chassagne murmured, '*Maintenant, c'est a moi*' (now its my turn), picked up a jack in each arm, ran back to the car, jacked it up and put the Bentley back in the running. On the last lap of all Birkin beat the lap record to run the car into fifth place—'A pleasant little triumph,' he commented.

By now Birkin had become fascinated by supercharging, seeing it as the easiest way of increasing the power and speed of the 4½-litre Bentley: he had obtained backing from the Hon.

Dorothy Paget and set up a factory at Welwyn, where the first supercharged conversion of the 4½-litre was built in 1928-9. However, it was with an unblown 6½-litre Bentley that Birkin achieved his most notable victory of the season—first place at Le Mans, partnered by Woolf Barnato.

The first appearance of the 'Blower Bentley' was at the Essex Six-Hours Race at Brooklands on 29 June 1929. The car retired, but the supercharger was shown to have given 'an increase of 100 hp—35 of which it required for itself—and a far swifter acceleration'. The top speed was also raised from 108 to 125 mph—'more than worth the trouble', opined Birkin. W. O. Bentley, however, wasn't so sure: 'To supercharge a Bentley engine is to pervert its design and corrupt its performance'.

In the Irish Grand Prix in July, Birkin, in 'No. 1 Blower Bentley', hounded 'Scrap' Thistlethwayte's supercharged 6.8-litre Mercedes to such good effect that the German car retired with a blown gasket. Boris Ivanowsky's Alfa had too great a lead on handicap, however, and won, with Glen Kidston's Speed Six Bentley second and Birkin third.

No. 1 Blower was adapted, in 1929, for Brooklands work (even though Birkin hated the track, it being 'out-of-date, inadequate and dangerous') with a narrow fabric covered two-seater body, which caught fire when the flexible exhaust pipe

broke in the 1929 500 Miles Race. This body was therefore replaced with a single-seat shell designed by Reid Railton. The engine had now been tuned to give more than twice the power of the standard 4½-litre unit.

Birkin had persuaded Bentley to produce a series of 50 blown cars to qualify the model for entry in the 1930 Le Mans 24 hours.

During the 1930 season, Birkin began a series of assaults on the Brooklands lap record, then held by Kaye Don's V12 Sunbeam Tiger. On his first attempt, Birkin lapped at 135.3 mph, beating the record, and then flew back to Le Touquet to claim the dinner Barnato had promised him if he exceeded Don's speed.

At Le Mans in June, Birkin led the harrying of Caracciola's Mercedes, a Bentley tactic which led to the German's withdrawal, although Birkin threw a tyre tread as he was overhauling Caracciola, running for several miles on the canvas at 125 mph. Birkin's car, having eventually fallen back to seventh place, retired after 20 hours when a con-rod broke and punched a hole in the crankcase.

The end of the Bentley company was now becoming increasingly apparent, and Dorothy Paget withdrew her support from the Blower team in October 1930, although she continued to back the single-seat No. 1 car. Birkin saw the season out in appropriate style by bringing a Blower 4½ into second place in the French Grand Prix at Pau against the far lighter and more manoeuvrable Bugattis.

Tim Birkin tried his hand with a Bugatti at Brooklands, in the Gold Star Handicap, but was disqualified after he had apparently won. In 1931, he eventually settled on an Alfa-Romeo for sports car events and a Maserati for Grands Prix. Partnered by Lord Howe, he won Le Mans in the Alfa, came fourth in the Belgian GP, with the Hon Brian Lewis as co-driver, and crashed in the Ulster TT.

The 1932 season saw the single-seat Blower Bentley out at Easter, when Birkin at last managed to crack the Outer Circuit record again, with a speed that was to stand for two years, a remarkable 137.96 mph, only beaten by John Cobb's 24-litre Napier-Railton.

In June, Birkin drove a new 2.3 Alfa and won the second day of the Dublin, Phoenix Park, races. He retired at Le Mans, however, with a blown head gasket.

At the end of July, Birkin's Bentley and John Cobb's Delage had a famous challenge match at Brooklands, which Birkin won by 25 yards after a 137 mph lap. It was one of the most enjoyable races of Birkin's career.

In 1933, he took delivery of a new 8C 3000 Maserati, with which he came third in the Tripoli Grand Prix, behind Nuvolari and Varzi. During practice he burned his arm against the exhaust-pipe while picking up his cigarette lighter. The wound turned septic, hastened by the effects of malaria which he had contracted in wartime while serving with the Royal Flying Corps in Palestine.

Early in June 1933, Birkin, his arm still bandaged after treatment, threw one of his customary parties at Ciro's Club, but the septicaemia spread and, on the 22nd of the same month, he died in the Countess Caernarvon Nursing Home in London. DBW

# Flying without wings

The courageous and tragic Bluebird legend was born from the dreams of a famous father and his equally famous son who dedicated their lives to the ceaseless quest for speed

IN 1912 MAURICE MAETERLINCK's play *The Bluebird* was premiered in London; among the audience was a rich young motor-racing enthusiast named Malcolm Campbell, who was so struck by the play that he decided to name his latest Brooklands car, a 59.6 hp Darracq, after it.

The Darracq, which he had bought direct from the makers, had been built for the 1909 Vanderbilt Cup race in America, and had a 10,567 cc engine, capable of reaching 100 mph at only 1200 rpm. It won its first two races for Campbell, who felt that the car's nickname was so lucky that he christened most of his subsequent racing and record-breaking cars with it.

Even so, on August Bank Holiday 1912, Bluebird's luck ran out. Coming up fast to the junction where the Finishing Straight left the Brooklands Outer Circuit, Campbell hit the concrete kerb with his off-side wheels, which flew to pieces—before each race they had to be soaked in water to make the wooden spokes fit into the rims more tightly—leaving the car skidding up the track on its hubs. Amazingly, it finished fifth in the race!

This first Bluebird was subsequently sold to the author G. N. R. Minchin, who rebuilt it as a touring car; after the war it was burned out in Ireland and the engine found its way into a boat.

In 1920, Campbell returned to Brooklands and, in 1921, the Bluebird name was transferred to a single-seat, 25 hp Talbot, sister car to the one used by Percy Lambert to set up the 100 miles in an hour record in 1913.

More famous, however, was Campbell's next Bluebird, the V12, 350 hp, aero-engined Sunbeam, originally built in 1920 by Louis Coatalen, which in the hands of Kenelm Lee Guinness had set up a new land-speed record of 133.75 mph at Brooklands in May 1922.

With this car Campbell attempted, in 1923, to set up a new world record on the beach at Fanö Island, off Denmark, but though the car reached 143 mph, the speed was not officially recognised. When Campbell returned to Fanö the following year, a wheel flew off into the crowd, killing a small boy. However, a subsequent attempt in the latter part of 1924 was more successful, when the Sunbeam achieved 146.16 mph on Pendine Sands, Carmarthenshire, beating the land-speed record of 146.01 mph, briefly held by Ernest

Eldridge's 300 hp Fiat, Mephistopheles.

Shortly afterwards, Campbell reached an average of 150.87 mph at Pendine with the Sunbeam, making this the first car officially to exceed 150 mph.

Within a few months, however, Campbell had lost the record again, to the 4-litre Sunbeam Tiger driven by H. O. D. Segrave and, by the end of 1926, Parry Thomas had raised the speed level to 171 mph. This was beyond the capabilities of the old Sunbeam; Campbell had already decided to go ahead with a purpose-built land-speed-record contender, work on which started in the early winter of 1924. Owing to a lack of facilities in the garage workshop in Campbell's house, the car was not completed until the end of December 1926.

In its first form, driven by a 620 hp Napier Lion aero-engine with twelve cylinders set in three banks of four in 'broad-arrow' configuration, the new Bluebird managed, in 1927, to set up a new world record of 174.88 mph at Pendine, despite a full-speed skid on one attempt, only to be totally eclipsed by Segrave's

*Top:* 1927, and Malcom Campbell is ready to attack the world land-speed record in his Campbell-Napier Bluebird. It would be a few years, though, before young Donald graduated to anything faster than his pedal car

*Above:* the Campbell-Railton-Rolls-Royce Bluebird, which achieved an average speed of 272.46 mph in 1933

*Previous page:* Donald Campbell and the last of the record-breaking Bluebird cars

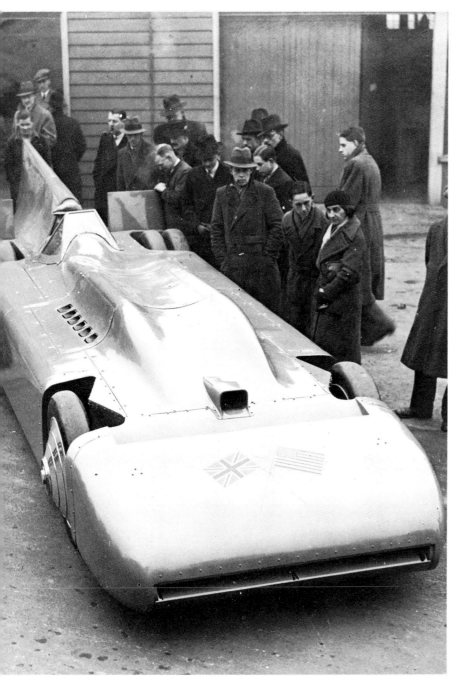

Developed in the wind-tunnel of the Vickers Aviation Company's experimental workshops, the body had a blunt nose 'like that of a large boot', blending into an oval-sectioned streamline, which tapered away into a pointed tail surmounted by a huge stabilising fin. The driving seat, above the leading edge of the rear tyres, was protected by a streamlined fairing: external radiators were carried on either side of the fin, in a position determined by the wind tunnel tests to be the most efficient. Fairings were fitted behind the wheels. The shape of the bodywork had been devised not for the most effective air penetration, but to give the car the maximum directional stability at 200 mph, and to press the car down on the ground when it was at full speed. Campbell beat Segrave's record with this car, reaching 206.96 mph at Daytona early in 1928, but the car's scientific design was again defeated by brute force, this time in the shape of Ray Keech's colossal, three-engined, 36-cylindered, 81-litre White Triplex, which raised the record to 207.55 mph the same year. In 1929, Segrave put the land-speed record even further out of reach with the Irving-Napier Golden Arrow, which averaged 231.44 mph.

Meanwhile, Campbell had modified the Bluebird still further, and had yet another body built, but a search for a new speed track in the Sahara in October 1928 nearly ended in disaster, when a crash in his Moth biplane left Campbell and his co-pilot, Flight-lieutenant Don, in the hands of Riff tribesmen. A few days after his eventual return home, Campbell received a telegram informing him that a perfect course existed at Verneuk Pan, in South Africa, in the bed of a vast dried-up lake. In February 1929, he arrived at Cape Town with Bluebird in an enormous packing case, a light plane, 36 tyres, 400 spark plugs, 500 gallons of petrol, the same amount of oil, the RAC's electrical timing apparatus (plus two official timekeepers) and five mechanics.

The Verneuk Pan site turned out to have been completely misrepresented: its hard-baked mud surface was crazed with heat-cracks, very uneven, and littered with sharp flints. It took a month's work by 500 workmen to make the eleven-mile course even approximately level; Campbell flew to Cape Town to make arrangements, found on arrival that the propeller of his plane had cracked in the heat and arranged to fly back in a friend's Avro Avian—which hit a tree on the homeward journey. Campbell flew back to Cape Town a few days later; the aircraft was overturned on landing by a gust of wind, tipping him out on his head and compounding his injuries. Then the worst rainstorm for 27 years washed out the Verneuk Pan course, followed by the news of Segrave's success at Daytona. Finally, after ten days of wind storms had ripped most of Campbell's tents to pieces, he managed to make his record attempt. His average, remarkable enough under the circumstances, was 218.9 mph, but it wasn't enough to beat Segrave's new record, though Campbell did manage to establish new five-kilometre and five-mile records of 216.5 and 212.8 mph respectively. On the journey home Campbell's touring car was completely wrecked in a collision on a mountain pass.

In 1931, Campbell, by now Sir Malcolm, raised the land-speed record to 246.09 mph at Daytona with the old Napier-Campbell, modified still further. The following year, with a new Napier power unit, he beat 250 mph for the first time, his actual speed being 253.97 mph. Within a few months, Bluebird had been virtually rebuilt, using a much more powerful engine— a supercharged Rolls-Royce R-Type V12, originally intended for the Supermarine S6b, which had won the

*Above:* this Campbell-Rolls-Royce Bluebird was the last of Sir Malcolm's record-breakers and it was in this car that he set a new record of 301.13 mph at the Bonneville Salt Flats in 1935. The intake slot in the nose could be closed for additional streamlining and the wheel fairings formed part of the main body. The car was powered by a supercharged, 2500 hp, V12 Rolls-Royce engine

latest mount, the 44-litre twin-engined Sunbeam, which broke the 200 mph barrier at Daytona Beach, Florida, on 29 March 1927, with a speed of 203.79 mph.

Campbell at once began remodelling his car, by having the engine rebuilt with an increased compression ratio so that it was in the same state of tune as the power unit of the Supermarine S5 seaplane that had won the 1927 Schneider Trophy. Only the massive chassis of the car remained unchanged: the front axle, damped by four Hartford friction shock absorbers, was fitted above the front springs, there were two independent steering gears, with a drop-arm for each front wheel, and the built-up rear axle was mounted above the chassis and back springs. The engine drove through an epicyclic gearbox, designed by Joseph Maina, in which the gear trains were positively locked in engagement; for 1928 this transmission, which had given considerable trouble in 1927, was modified to give a quick getaway. However, the most interesting feature of the 1928 Napier-Campbell Bluebird was the streamlined bodywork built by Barker and Company.

*Near right:* the first
post-war Bluebird car
was built for Donald
Campbell by the Norris
Brothers. Known as the
Carnpbell-Norris-Proteus
Bluebird, it was fitted
with a 5000 hp Bristol
Proteus turbine engine.
At the Bonneville Salt
Flats on 16 September
1960, Donald, in an
attempt to beat the
world land-speed
record, crashed the car
at over 360 mph but
escaped almost
uninjured

*Far right:* following
Donald Campbell's
spectacular accident at
Bonneville in 1960, the
Bluebird was rebuilt and
a tail fin added for
stability. After much
testing and a further
unsuccessful attempt on
the world record, the
Bluebird was taken to
Lake Eyre in Australia
where, on 17 July 1964,
Donald achieved an
average speed for a
two-way run of 403.1
mph to gain the official
world land-speed
record

Schneider Trophy outright in 1931. With a swept
volume of 36½ litres, the engine developed around
2500 bhp. Its sheer size posed considerable installation
problems, so that a radiator had to be fitted in the nose
of the lengthened chassis, supplemented by a water
tank above the front axle and built round the supercharger housing. An all-indirect, offset, three-speed
gearbox brought the propeller shaft close to the
left-hand chassis side member to allow sufficient room
for the driver's seat; the stabilising fin was set to the
right, behind the cockpit. As much weight as possible
was added to the chassis to hold it down at the car's
designed maximum speed of 280 mph: armour-plate
cross-members were added at the nose, while 'enormous blocks of lead' were packed into the frame
members and around the back axle. The wheels,
turned from steel, were so heavy that two men were
needed to lift each one, and built-in jacks were fitted
at each corner of the frame. It was stated that at top
speed the three-foot-diameter tyres would 'grow' by
about an inch under the influence of centrifugal force,
and that the kinetic energy of the car, said to be
around 23,000,000 lb ft at full speed, was sufficient to
propel an ordinary touring car 20 miles at 40 mph.

Though the car broke the record at Daytona, with
an average of 272.46 mph, it was not fast enough for
Campbell, who was aiming to be first driver to top
300 mph. During 1934, Bluebird was again rebuilt,
with streamlined bodywork extended to the full width
of the axles, but still with the wheels exposed. New
features included twin rear wheels for better adhesion
and a duplicated final drive, without a differential.

The body panelling was supported on a tubular
framework bolted to the chassis, and it encased twin
outrigged 40-gallon fuel tanks. Vacuum-servo braking
was now fitted, supplemented by servo-operated flaps
which acted as air brakes, and also gave extra down-
thrust on the rear wheels. For extra speed, a flap closed
the slot in the nose which admitted air to the radiator,
reducing wind resistance as the car rushed over the
measured mile at over 400 feet per second.

In 1935, Bluebird achieved 276.82 mph at Daytona,
but it was apparent that the limit on this sand course
had been reached. Campbell tried again later in the
year, on the new speed course at the Bonneville Salt
Flats in Utah, and achieved his ambition by setting up
a new record of 301.13 mph, covering a mile in 11.83
seconds.

This was Sir Malcolm Campbell's last land-speed
record, but, though he was now over 50, he turned his
attention to a new element, and set up water-speed
records on three occasions, driving Rolls-Royce-
engined Bluebird motor boats: in 1937, he achieved
124.86 mph; in 1938 raised it to 130.86 mph and in
1939 set up a record of 141.7 mph.

After his death, in 1949, his son Donald continued
the Bluebird tradition breaking the water-speed
record several times with a new jet-propelled Bluebird
boat.

It wasn't until 1960 that Donald Campbell concentrated on the land-speed record with a 5000 hp four-
wheeled car powered by a Bristol Proteus free-turbine
engine and designed by the Norris Brothers of
Burgess Hill, Sussex. Donald's first run in a record-
breaking car was on 5 September 1960 at Utah Salt
Flats, when he took the mighty car to a leisurely
120 mph on a shakedown run. Just eleven days later,
Donald set out again, this time in a bid to break the
record, although it was against the advice of Dunlop
engineer Don Badger who said that 300 mph was the
limit for the tyres fitted. The car had only covered 1.6
miles when disaster struck.

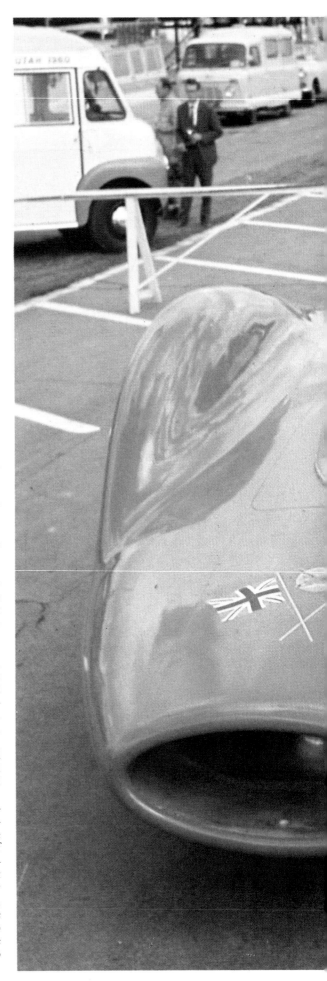

The car, which was travelling in excess of 360 mph, wavered off line, took off, and virtually flew for almost 300 yards before crashing to the ground and 'bouncing' a further four times before coming to rest over half a mile away from where it first ran out of control. Almost all of it was destroyed apart from the immensely strong cockpit structure which allowed Campbell to escape almost uninjured.

By November 1961 the car was rebuilt with further aerodynamic aids added. During the time up until May 1963, it was extensively tested, and preparations were made for another attempt on the record at Lake Eyre, Australia. Almost immediately after the Bluebird entourage started to prepare for the attempt, a storm broke over the area and the salt flat was completely flooded. The party returned the following year and after much testing, Donald broke the record on 17 July at an average speed for a two-way run of 403.1 mph.

Donald Campbell went to Coniston Water, Westmorland, for a further crack at the water-speed record with the old Bluebird boat on 4 January 1967. While travelling at a speed well in excess of 300 mph the bows of the boat lifted and the Bluebird somersaulted, ending up almost completely disintegrated. Campbell's body was never found.

The Campbells are gone, so are the record-breaking days of Bluebird, probably the most famous record breaker ever. They will never be forgotten.      DBW

# THE LONG AND WINDING ROAD

Today, BMW is one of the world's most successful and prosperous motoring manufacturers. It wasn't always so: the company has had its ups and downs

THE BAYERISCHE MOTOREN WERKE is not one of the old, original European car firms; in fact BMW came on the scene relatively late, in 1916. Nor was it a company which was founded by a single visionary. Instead, it has its origins rooted in the development of two complementary companies and it made its reputation in racing and record breaking in various spheres. History has shown that companies which race always attract attention—either for winning or for skirting bankruptcy. BMW came very close to achieving both.

After each world war, the Bavarian factory managed to survive through occupation eras, years of industrial and financial depression and often poor management decisions, to ward off merger bids and rise again, independent and, eventually, successful.

Any study of BMW history must begin with aviation; the company's badge is based on the stylized blur of a spinning propeller, picked out in the Bavarian State colours of blue and white. The BMW story began when a German named Gustav Otto founded an aero-

plane factory on the outskirts of Munich in 1911. In 1913, another German, Karl Rapp, opened a factory nearby to build marine and aviation engines. The two companies moved closer together in March 1916, when Otto formed the Bayerische Flugzeug Werke, building military aircraft powered by Rapp engines, and by the next summer Rapp had turned his operation into the Bayerische Motoren Werke.

At the end of World War I, BMW turned to manufacturing airbrakes for German railroads, while BFW started to build tool cabinets and office furniture. The two companies remained separate but co-operative entities until 1922, when a Viennese banker called Castiglioni bought them both.

Max Friz of BMW, who had worked on the Daimler Grand Prix engine in 1917, designed a small ohc four-cylinder engine, for boats, buses and stationary uses, which was so sturdy that the company was still filling spares orders 30 years after the engine was put into production. Friz also produced a 500 cc, horizontally-opposed, twin-cylinder unit, again intended for

*Above left:* the first four-wheeled BMW, the 1928 Dixi, was an Austin 7 built under licence.

*Above:* the business-like 507 coupé produced 150 bhp from a 3168 cc, V8 engine. The car was used in hill-climbs by Hans Stuck, albeit with little success

*Right:* the Dixi Roadster had a top speed of 65 mph and was fairly successful in competition, winning its class in the 1930 Monte Carlo rally

*Left:* the BMW badge is a stylized blur of a spinning aeroplane propeller in the Bavarian State colours. BMW's East German contemporaries, EMW (previously named BMW) used the same badge finished in red and white

stationary use, but a company called Victoria put this 'Bayermotor' into a motor-cycle frame—lengthwise.

BFW had been thinking along the same lines and had built a motor cycle utilizing the same engine, calling the finished model the Helios. It had even put into production a motor cycle with a two-stroke, single-cylinder engine called the Flink. Following BMW's merger with BFW, Friz was instructed to improve the Helios which he personally considered to be beyond saving. Company legend has it that he sketched an all-new alternative design on the back of a beer mat.

From that simple beginning, the foundations for yet another chapter in the history of BMW were laid—one which is still progressing. The new design was called the BMW R32 and was introduced to the public at the 1923 Paris Salon. The main technical features employed, such as a transverse twin-cylinder engine in unit with the gearbox, combined with shaft-drive, were not original, but the Friz combination of them in a 265 lb, side-valve, 500 cc touring motor cycle was, and this basic layout is still used for current BMW production motor cycles.

In 1926, the company introduced the ohv R37 and BMW won a Gold Medal in the Six-Day Trial event, the first ever for Germany. All told, eight versions of this machine were built in the first five years of production, nearly 28,000 were sold and 573 competitive events were won.

More important than the company's success on two wheels was the fact that in 1928 BMW went into the car business, albeit by the acquisition of the Dixi company and a licence to manufacture that company's design. The Dixi was the vehicle with which BMW embarked upon its four-wheel career. Available as a roadster or as an open tourer, it was actually the British Austin 7 manufactured under licence. BMW won its class, with this car, in the 1930 Monte Carlo Rally.

That was not the first success for the BMW miniature, of which over 25,000 were to be sold by 1932: before sales had even begun, the company had entered three cars in the 1929 Alpine Trial and taken the team prize from 200 starters. A contemporary BMW Dixi would do 55 mph and there was a 65 mph Sport model available as well.

By 1932, customers were being offered the 3/20PS model of 20 bhp, and a year later came the first of the company's famous six-cylinder cars, the 1175 cc, 30 bhp 303 model. This was soon enlarged to a 1.5-litre 315 model fitted with twin carburettors and a four-speed gearbox.

The first really famous BMW motor car was the 315 roadster, a car capable of reaching 75 mph, which won the Alpine Trial as well as enjoying success in many other sporting events of the time. Basically a simple car, the BMW 315 had a 1490 cc, six-cylinder engine producing 34 bhp. Drum brakes were fitted all round. The tax laws prevailing in Germany at the

193

time dictated that a 900cc engine should also be available, but the star of the company's expanding range was the 319, which was introduced in 1936. When fitted with two carburettors, the 1875 cc engine produced 45 bhp, while a three-carburettor version was capable of producing 55 bhp.

The next important stage in the company's development was later in 1936, when a two-litre engine of 1975 cc was offered as the 326 model complete with a sports-touring body. A simpler 320/321 version had only two doors and a single carburettor, but this range was the first from BMW to feature the marque's now-distinctive 'vertical ovals' grille.

As such cars edged towards sporting prominence, BMW motor cycles were also winning international laurels. In 1929, Henne, already a circuit champion and 1928 motor cycle Targa Florio winner, became the first German to claim the absolute two-wheel speed record, on a BMW 750 twin.

He went on to set the mark six more times, eventually leaving it at 174 mph in 1937, achieved with a supercharged 500 cc twin. BMW had at first tried a Rootes blower and then a Zoller unit and by 1945 was even contemplating a blown 50 bhp, 500 cc Six-Day Trial bike.

Henne moved from two wheels to four in 1936, making his debut at the Nürburgring in a 328. He won the two-litre class first time out, driving against pure racing cars, and by 1939 the starting grid for the Nürburgring race found BMW 328s occupying the first four rows.

Recognizing the potential, BMW decided to develop those cars and began with the 326/327 coupé and cabriolet models which produced 55 bhp. By fitting light-alloy cylinder heads with overhead valves opened by cross-over pushrods, larger ports and three Solex carburettors, the engines were improved enough to produce 80 bhp at 4700 rpm. This gave the cars a top speed of 95 mph, in normal customer trim, and the ability to cruise all day at 4000 rpm and 80 mph on the autobahn. Customers could choose which set of gear ratios they wanted by specifying either a ZF or Hirth gearbox.

Four of these cars started the 1938 Mille Miglia, finishing 7th, 9th, 10th and 11th overall to sweep their class. The same model won the Spa 24-hour race and went to Le Mans in 1939 with the first streamlined coupé bodies seen at the circuit, taking fifth place

overall. With 100 bhp engines these cars could reach 125 mph and it was just such a 328 that scored the marque's crowning pre-war victory, coming first overall in the Brescia Mille Miglia of 1940.

So ended the pre-war story of BMW except for the introduction of the 335 model. Announced in 1939 and fitted with a 3.5-litre six-cylinder engine developing 90 bhp, it was the largest BMW made up to that point.

In the aftermath of World War II, sheer survival took precedence over new-car production. The Allies declared that BMW should never rise again and they were nearly right: skilled men were occupied producing cooking pots and farm machinery rather than working on a wild BMW scheme to produce a turbine-engined locomotive. The company's old workshops were taken over and became repair centres for the vehicles of the US Army.

However, technical expertise would not be denied and even during those grim days the company was producing bicycles cast in aluminium—a few were made with even-lighter electron frames, but lack of tooling prevented volume production.

The directors of BMW still nurtured plans to get back into the motor industry however, and they leaned towards producing a prestige car, ignoring the loss of parts and plans to Russian control in Eisenach which, after the war, became part of the German Democratic Republic. By late 1945, this Eastern plant was planning to manufacture a copy of the 321, while the original BMW company could think only about producing motor cycles. In 1949, the Eisenach factory built the 340 model which featured an American-type radiator grille and a fascia-mounted gear change. The company even showed a 328 coupé and an SI dream car, which featured a plexiglass top. The makers claimed that 130 bhp was produced from a developed 328 engine—but didn't say how. These last two cars were never marketed, but the East Germans did export the 340 to Sweden, Belgium and Switzerland. The Munich-based directors of the original BMW company were furious when customers applied to them for spare parts. Eventually, legal action forced the Eisenach company to become EMW and the badge to be a quartered red and white circle.

Meanwhile, BMW's chief designer, Fiedler, had been lost to Bristol, although the Munich company retained the rights to any 328 development work used in Bristol's 400 model. Lacking blueprints, which had

*Above:* the 1934 315/1 Sport had a 6-cylinder, 1490 cc engine that produced 40 bhp. In competition trim, the car was highly successful and it put BMW firmly on the motor-sport map

*Below:* the 6-cylinder, 55 bhp coupé of 1937 was a successful adaptation of the race-winning 328. It was a prime example of how racing improves the breed

been lost, the design staff of BMW could only dream about a Kamm-tailed K-1 model which would have followed the 326 but for World War II. German news reporters further irritated the directors of the Munich company in 1947 by calling the Veritas, which featured a tuned 328 engine, a 'new BMW'. This small, specialist firm built road cars, sports racers and Formula Two cars and was successful in all classes, but it could not sustain itself and eventually disappeared like so many others.

Other companies continued to utilize the basic potential of the BMW six-cylinder engine. AFM used the engine in a single-seater racing car which went quite fast but, unfortunately, not for very long. Frazer-Nash and Arnolt-Bristol similarly annoyed the hierarchy by fitting the motor-cycle engine into half a dozen miniature monoposto racing cars.

Feeling threatened on all sides, and with its finances and productive capacity still in an uncertain condition, the management of BMW debated whether to merge with another company—originally preferring Bristol which was not interested in the proposal, but which did release Fiedler from his contract. BMW even talked to Auto Union, who wanted to formulate a common policy of two-stroke production. BMW found this proposal unacceptable and declined to proceed further with it. Another plan to build a small Simca fell through over tooling and the company lacked sufficient experience for a proposed Ford truck venture to be pursued.

Ford, Opel, Mercedes and Volkswagen had long since returned to production when BMW realized that the company could not afford to tool up for a mass-production motor car. A proposed two-litre, four-cylinder car was therefore out. Instead, BMW decided to build a small run of exclusive machines powered by

*Below:* the 328 'Mille Miglia'. By 1940, the 328 had been developed into a highly successful race-winner. With a 100 bhp engine and a top speed of 125 mph, the car won the 1940 Brescia Mille Miglia

the old, but still reasonably potent, six-cylinder unit, a thousand spare 326 blocks having been cast for just this purpose.

This new model was designated the 501 and featured a fairly modest output from the engine, although an aluminium block V8 unit was running on the test bench early in 1949. BMW also commissioned a Pininfarina body, but used their own design because the Italian proposal looked remarkably like an Alfa Romeo.

It was also around this time that the management vetoed a Fiedler designed, Fiat Topolino-like, two-seat prototype powered by the company's twin-cylinder motor-cycle engine.

The 501 model quickly earned a reputation for technical superiority even though it was too slow by the standards of the day. Priced at 50 times the

average monthly wage of the German worker at that time, it cost far too much to reach its projected yearly sales. The V8 engine was delayed owing to a lack of finance and efforts to improve the six-cylinder engine brought only failure.

By 1954, a 100 mph top speed was considered to be essential by the board of the company and the 502 model, with a 2.6 V8, was introduced in the same year. In 1955, BMW added the 503 coupé and 507 model to the range, but not even the recall of Hans Stuck to claim some hill-climb titles in a 507 could sell enough of them. Not did the company have any better luck with the 505 model intended for VIPs and statesmen—two limousine prototypes were built by Ghia-Aigle but resistance from the market at which the car was aimed meant that the model was never put into production.

Casting around for new avenues of expansion, BMW took a close look at the Isetta bubble car and decided that the company had the necessary expertise and facilities to produce it. It arranged a licence to produce them powered by the 250 cc motor-cycle engine with a fan cooling. These small, unusual cars proved to be quite popular for a short while, probably because the rise in the standard of living of so many Germans meant that they could now afford to become mobile once more. However, with the ever increasing rise in the standard of living which was a strong feature of Germany throughout the fifties and sixties, people soon began to demand four seats and a more car-like shape than the Isetta could provide. What the public couldn't appreciate, however, was the over-engineered BMW 600 which was produced as an attempt to satisfy that demand.

This, of course, caused further financial difficulties for the company and, when motor-cycle turnover, spare part sales and US Forces rents all declined, the banks which had supported the board of BMW

suggested that the company be sold to Mercedes-Benz and it was left to the small shareholders in the company to frustrate that particular manoeuvre.

Perhaps by luck, but maybe by judgement, the answer to BMW's pressing financial problems was already in the prototype stage, in the shape of the Michelotti-designed BMW 700 which was first introduced in coupé form—even though the older members of the BMW board at first resisted its introduction. Powered by a rear-mounted, 697 cc air-cooled engine which developed 30 bhp, it provided a lively means of transport to the poorer members of the rapidly growing German bourgeois class.

The car was even entered in competitions and the ageing Stuck was brought in to win just one more mountain hill-climb title with a developed version. With this success, BMW at last had a sporting image on which it could capitalise and it was quick to see the possibilities and the potential and to act upon them. BMW quickly introduced a four-door 1500 model powered by an 80 bhp engine featuring a single ohc, which was put on the market before BMW finally phased out its big saloon and coupé line—despite a still-born plan to fit a Lancia Flaminia body to the basic 1500 running gear. A massive success from its introduction, such was the popularity of the 1500 that production of all other motor cars ceased almost immediately, as the factory concentrated all its financial and industrial resources on penetrating the market as quickly and as deeply as possible.

The company did not ignore the fact that progress had to be made if it was to keep up the commercial pressure and therefore build a solid foundation from which to operate. An 1800 cc model was developed quickly, but properly, along with an 1800 TI variant, the latter winning both the first circuit race and the first hill-climb in which it was entered.

By the end of March 1964, when the BMW V8

*Above:* the 6-cylinder, 3½-litre 335 of 1939. Unfortunately, with the outbreak of war, production was suspended and only a few models were built

*Far right, top:* the pretty 2002 touring was introduced in 1971 as a 3-door sports-estate version of the popular 2002. It is available with a fuel-injected, or normally aspirated, 2-litre engine

*Far right, bottom:* the in-line, 6-cylinder 2500 was introduced in 1968 and is the basis for all subsequent 3-litre saloons and coupés

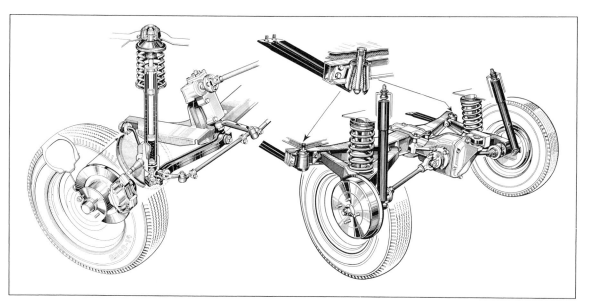

*Right:* the front and rear suspension systems of the BMW 1500 and 1800. The front is independent with MacPherson struts and telescopic dampers. Rear is also independent by semi-trailing arms, coil springs and telescopic dampers

*Below:* a cutaway of the 1963 1800. This sports-saloon was introduced as a direct competitor to the Italian Alfa Romeos

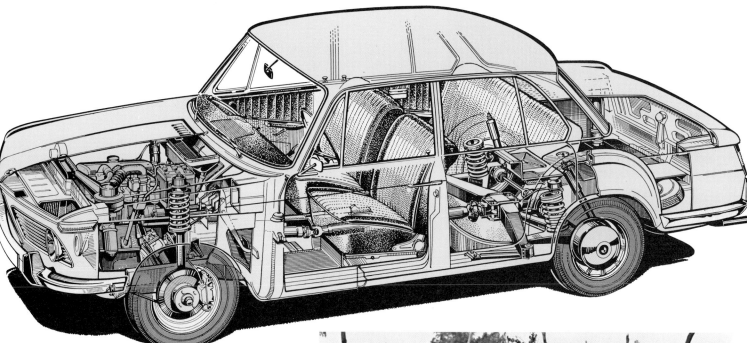

and the Isetta had been firmly buried, BMW enjoyed the best growth rate of any German manufacturer, even though the company had yet to crack the big limousine market. There was, however, the 2000 CS coupé, the forerunner to a 2-litre saloon, but a special Glas model, powered by the old V8 engine and introduced at the Frankfurt Motor Show of 1965, had attracted enormous attention and represented potential competition. However, Glas was in trouble and, although a few years earlier the Bavarian State had asked Glas to buy out BMW—and been refused—the bureaucrats had no compunction in now asking BMW to help Glas.

Seeing the potential, BMW agreed and at first promised to up-date the Glas quality and to retain all Glas models. But the Glas line was soon pruned to a GT car, powered by a 2600 BMW engine and given the same badge and independent rear suspension, a V8 model enlarged to 3 litres and the Goggomobil, a small economy vehicle still quite popular among lower paid workers. It was perhaps fortunate that the South African outlet of BMW wanted to build a cheaper car

and this company was given the Glas 1700 tooling plus a supply of BMW engines and badges. 1968 saw the demise of Glas as a separate entity.

Even before that, BMW was moving so fast that the company introduced a 2000 model saloon, to mark the 50th anniversary of the company's founding, as well as a two door 1600–2, yet another hugely successful model which was to capture both track records and customers alike. That particular model became the basis for the 1602, 1802 and 2002 models and even a fastback estate version called the Touring, a sure sign of the company's increasing control of its market area and its own policies.

By linking itself very successfully to a sporting image and taking the care to trasnfer this image to big, comfortable and very fast saloons and coupés BMW rapidly built up an enormously strong market position. The 2002 model took the European Saloon Car Racing Championship in 1969 and another version of the model became the first turbocharged BMW to be offered to private customers. BMW also turned to single-seater racing, in 1974, with an F2 engine which later captured not only many first places but also many records. However, the company's success in racing circles was based primarily on the BMW range of touring cars, which also proved to be eminently suitable for tuning by a wide range of European tuning specialists, both in Germany and elsewhere.

Such was, and is, the strength of the company that over the past few years it has been asked to help or take over several other motor manufacturers, as well as being a first-class contender in the merger stakes. Lack of capital led to BMW turning down an approach to take over Lancia, and fears that a US-built car would lack the German mystique cancelled a project planned with American Motors. Nor did BMW join with DAF which would have given the company a foothold in the lucrative European truck market.

What increasing profitability did mean for BMW was that the engineers could turn back to their first love, the in-line six-cylinder engine. This unit was first introduced in a completely redesigned form in the 2500 saloon in 1968. The success of the car and the quality of the basic design soon led to the engine being enlarged to 2.8 and then to 3 litres, this unit powering both coupé and saloon versions. The 2500 was also the first BMW to be equipped with disc brakes on all four wheels.

These and other items, such as fuel injection, aerofoils and air dams introduced on the latest BMWs, have all combined to give the BMW racing department sufficient edge to beat all comers in the European Touring Car Championship of 1973.

For the future, BMW has introduced the Turbo prototype, an advanced wedge-shaped coupé with gull-wing doors, deformable crush zones, a turbocharged engine and a cockpit instrument display panel featuring digital read-out instruments.

Other new models continue to pour off the Bavarian production lines in an ever increasing flood of potentially exciting cars. The 520 saloon, introduced in 1972 with a four-cylinder engine, soon received the company's very popular six-cylinder unit—becoming in the process the 525 model. The company has even found the time, money and space needed to build a long chassis, executive saloon with the designation 3.3L.

BMW products are intended for drivers who enjoy driving—in fact it was this market which was picked with great care when the foundations for the company's recent successes were laid in the very early sixties.                                                     JS

*Above:* the sleek Turbo Coupé is a styling exercise based on 2002 turbo mechanicals

*Left:* the 520, introduced in 1972, is the successor to the 2000 range

*Below:* A Schnitzer BMW 2002 similar to the car that won the 1969 Touring Car Championship

*Bottom:* a 'naked' 3.0CSL. This car had most of its aerodynamic wings removed at Monza, where they would have hindered the straight-line speed on the very fast circuit

## The 2002

The BMW 2002 range is the most popular of all the German company's offerings. The body shape has been in production since 1966.

The present 2002 range comprises the standard 2002, the 2002 tii with fuel injection, the convertible 2002 cabriolet and the supercharged 2002 turbo. All these use the same basic body-chassis unit, but there is a further version, the 2002 touring, which uses a later body.

The power unit for all these models is a 1990 cc straight-four, with a single overhead camshaft opening the valves. Power output ranges from 100 bhp (DIN) for the saloon to 170 bhp (DIN) for the turbocharged car which can only be supplied in left-hand-drive form, due to the position of the exhaust-driven turbocharger.

The front-mounted engine drives a four-speed, or five-speed, all-synchromesh gearbox through a single-plate hydraulic clutch and, from there, the propeller shaft feeds the torque to a hypoid-bevel final drive.

Front suspension is taken care of by MacPherson struts, which include coil springs, auxiliary rubber springs and telescopic dampers. A lower wishbone is fitted, to prevent each wheel from swinging on the strut. At the rear, semi-trailing arms locate the wheels,

which again have coil springs, as well as rubber auxiliaries, and telescopic dampers. Double-jointed drive shafts take the final-drive output to the wheels.

Throughout the range, braking is by discs at the front and drums at the rear, with a dual-circuit hydraulic system and a vacuum servo. The handbrake operates on the rear drums, by means of cables.

Worm and roller steering is mounted behind the front wheels, for protection in the event of an accident, and the steering wheel is padded.

The saloon body has two doors and five seats—the front ones recline—while the touring has a third, rear, door with only four seats, the reclining backrests being extra. Construction is unitary.

ENGINE: Front-mounted, in-line four, water cooled. 89 mm (3.5 in) bore × 80 mm (3.15 in) stroke = 1990 cc (121.4 cu in). Maximum power 100 bhp (DIN) at 5500 rpm (standard and cabriolet), 130 bhp (DIN) at 5800 rpm (tii), 170 bhp (DIN) at 5800 rpm (turbo); maximum torque 113 lb ft at 3500 rpm (standard and cabriolet), 130 lb ft at 4500 rpm (tii), 177 lb ft at 4000 rpm (turbo). Cast-iron cylinder block and light-alloy head; compression ratio 8.5:1 (standard and cabriolet), 9.5:1 (tii), 6.9:1 (turbo); 5 main bearings. 2 valves per cylinder,

operated, via rockers, by 1 chain-driven overhead camshaft. 1 Solex downdraught carburettor (standard and cabriolet), Kugelfischer mechanical fuel injection (tii), Kugelfischer mechanical fuel injection with exhaust-driven turbocharger (turbo).

TRANSMISSION: Single-plate clutch; 4- or 5-speed, all-synchromesh gearbox (ratios—standard, cabriolet and tii 4-speed—1st 3.764, 2nd 2.02, 3rd 1.32, 4th 1.0, reverse 4.1:1 —turbo 4-speed 1st 3.35, 2nd 1.86, 3rd 1.28, 4th 1.0, reverse 3.65:1—5-speed 1st 3.37, 2nd 2.16, 3rd 1.58, 4th 1.24, 5th 1.0, reverse 4.0:1; hypoid-bevel final drive (ratio—standard, cabriolet and tii 3.64:1—turbo 3.36:1) to rear wheels.

CHASSIS: Monocoque body/chassis.

SUSPENSION: Front—independent by MacPherson coil-spring/damper struts, with rubber auxiliary springs and lower wishbones; rear—independent by semi-trailing arms, coil springs, rubber auxiliary springs and telescopic dampers.

STEERING: ZF Gemmer worm-and-roller; 3.5 turns from lock to lock.

BRAKES: Dual-circuit, hydraulically operated discs front and drums rear, with vacuum-servo

assistance; disc diameter 9.4 in, except turbo 10.1 in; drum diameter 9.0 in standard and cabriolet, 9.4 in tii, 9.84 in turbo; handbrake operating on rear wheels.

WHEELS: 5 in J × 13 pressed steel, except turbo $5\frac{1}{2}$ in J × 13; 6 in J × 13 aluminium alloy optional on turbo.

TYRES: 165SR × 13, except turbo 185/70VR × 13.

DIMENSIONS AND WEIGHT: Wheelbase 98.4 in; track front and rear 52.8, except turbo 53.6; length 166.5 in, except touring 161.8 in; width 62.6 in, except turbo 63.8 in; height 55.5 in, except cabriolet 53.5 in and touring 54.2; ground clearance 6.3 in; kerb weight 2183 lb standard and cabriolet, 2226 lb tii, 2270 lb touring, 2283 lb turbo; turning circle between walls 34 ft, except touring 32 ft, fuel tanks 11 gals, except turbo 15.4 gals.

BODY: Saloon or convertible; 2 or 3 doors; 4 or 5 seats.

PERFORMANCE: Maximum speed 106 mph standard and cabriolet, 115 mph tii, 131 mph turbo; 0–60 mph 9.2 secs standard and cabriolet, 8.2 secs tii, 6.5 secs turbo; standing $\frac{1}{4}$-mile 17.5 secs standard and cabriolet, 16.6 secs tii, 15.3 secs turbo; fuel consumption 28 mpg standard and cabriolet, 32 mpg tii, 29 mpg turbo.

## The 3-litres

The 3-litre BMWs, the top of the range, are based on two body styles: the four-door saloon, and two-door coupé. They are both powered by derivatives of the straight-six, seven-main-bearing, single-overhead-camshaft engine.

The range comprises the 3.0S automatic, 3.0Si and 3.3L saloons and the 3.0CS automatic, 3.0CSi and 3.0CSL coupés.

Power from the front-mounted engine is transmitted to the rear wheels via a four-speed synchromesh, or three-speed automatic gearbox and a hypoid-bevel final drive (a limited-slip differential is standard equipment on the 3.0CSL).

Independent front suspension on all models is by damper struts and lower wishbones, with coil springs and rubber auxiliary springs; ZF hydraulic power assistance takes the effort out of steering. The rear suspension is also independent, by means of semi-trailing arms and coil springs with rubber auxiliary springs and telescopic dampers (anti-roll bars are standard all round on coupés).

Stopping is taken care of by twin-circuit, servo assisted disc brakes; the discs being of the ventilated type. The handbrake works on separate drums.

The saloon body has four doors and ample room for five people. The front seats recline and the drivers seat is adjustable for height. Head restraints are standard equipment both front and rear. The two door coupé is a four-seater, all seats being body-contoured for lateral support in high-speed driving. The front seats also recline.

Body construction on all models is unitary. The 3.0CSL has a special lightweight body which features light-alloy doors, engine compartment lid and luggage compartment lid.

ENGINE: Front-mounted, in-line six, water cooled 80 mm (3.15 in) bore × 89 mm (3.504 in) stroke = 2985 cc (184.4 cu in) (3.0S, 3.0Si, 3.0CS and 3.0CSi), 84 mm (3.307 in) bore × 89.25 mm (3.514 in) stroke = 3153 cc (3.0CSL), 88.4 mm (3.480 in) bore × 89 mm (3.504 in) stroke = 3295 cc (201 cu in) (3.3L). Power output ranging from 180 bhp (3.0S and 3.0CS) to 206 bhp (3.0CSL); maximum torque ranging from 188 lb ft (3.0S and 3.0CS) to 213.3 lb ft (3.3L). Cast-iron cylinder block and light-alloy head; compression ratio 9.0:1 (3.0S, 3.0CS and 3.3L), 9.5:1 (3.0Si, 3.0CSi and 3.0CSL); 7 main bearings. 2 valves per cylinder, operated, via rockers, by 1 chain-driven overhead camshaft. 2 Solex or Zenith twin-choke carburettors (3.0S, 3.0CS and 3.3L) Bosch electronic fuel injection (3.0Si 3.0CSi and 3.0CSL).

TRANSMISSION: Single-dry-plate clutch; 4-speed all synchromesh gearbox (ratios 3.0Si, 3.0CSi and 3.0CSL—1st 3.855, 2nd 2.202, 3rd 1.401, 4th 1.0, reverse 4.3:1) or 3-speed automatic 3.0S, 3.0CS and 3.3L—1st 2.50, 2nd 1.50, 3rd 1.0:1); hypoid-bevel final drive (limited-slip differential optional, standard on 3.0CSL) ratio—3.0S, 3.0Si, 3.0CS and 3.3L, 3.45:1, ratio—3.0CSi and 3.0CSL, 3.25:1 to rear wheels.

CHASSIS: Monocoque body/chassis.

SUSPENSION: Front—independent by damper struts and lower wishbones with coil springs, rubber auxiliary springs and an anti-roll bar (coupé only); rear —independent by semi-trailing arms and coil springs with rubber auxiliary springs and telescopic dampers and an anti-roll bar (coupé only).

STEERING: ZF hydraulic power-assisted worm and nut steering; 4.4 turns from lock to lock.

BRAKES: Quadruple-circuit, hydraulically operated ventilated discs front and rear with twin servos; front and rear disc diameter 10.7 in; handbrake operating on rear wheels through separate drums.

WHEELS: 3.0S and 3.0Si, 6J × 14 H2 steel (light-alloy optional extra) 3.0CS, 3.0CSi and 3.3L 6J × 14 H2 light alloy, 3.0CSL 7J × 14 H2 Alpina light-alloy.

TYRES: 195/70 VR14 tubed (coupés) or 195HR14 tubed (saloons).

DIMENSIONS AND WEIGHT: Wheelbase, coupés 103.3 in, saloons (except 3.3L) 106 in, 3.3L 109.9 in; track front all models (except 3.0CSL) 56.9 in, 3.0CSL 57.9 in; track rear saloons 57.6 in, 3.0CS and 3.0CSi 55.2 in, 3.0CSL 56.1 in; length coupés 183.5 in, 3.0S and 3.0Si 185 in, 3.3L 189 in; width saloons 68.9 in, 3.0CS and 3.0CSi 65.7 in, 3.0CSL 68.1 in; height saloons 57.1 in, coupés 53.9 in; ground clearance all models 5.51 in; kerb weight 3.0CS and 3.0CSi 3042 lb, 3.0S 3086 lb, 3.0Si 3130 lb, 3.3L 3196 lb and 3.0CSL 2757 lb; turning circle between walls all models (except 3.3L) 34.5 ft, 3.3L 35.5 ft; fuel tank saloons 16.5 gals, coupés 15.8 gals.

BODY: Saloon or coupé; 2 or 4 doors; 4 or 5 seats.

PERFORMANCE: Maximum speed ranges between 127 mph (3.0S) and 138 mph (3.0CSL); 0–60 mph between 9.0 secs (3.0S) and 6.9 secs (3.0CSL); standing $\frac{1}{4}$-mile between 17.0 secs (3.0S) and 14.9 secs (3.0CSL); fuel consumption 24 mpg (approx) for all models.

The fastest model in the three-litre range is the 3.0 CSL, which comes complete with airfoils. In Germany, these 'wings' are illegal, so cars sold in that country have them in the boot

# KEEPING THE BODY BEAUTIFUL

No matter how well the mechanics of a car are maintained, its body is likely to suffer, either through rust or through rough treatment. However, restoration can be surprisingly easy

Any rust holes must be thoroughly cleaned up before filling. If the back of the panel cannot be reached, the edges of the holes must be hammered in to allow glassfibre and resin to be used. Brush the edges with resin and hardener, then apply a glassfibre patch just larger than each hole. Push the patch gently into the hole, using a stippling brush, dipped in resin and hardener, to impregnate the fibre

When the resin is dry, filler paste should be used to fill any remaining indentations. Allow the filler to stand slightly proud, then it can be rubbed down, using a file or wet-or-dry paper, until it matches the body contours. Any minor imperfections will have to be refilled

*Left:* the filler should now be rubbed down with progressively finer grades of wet-or-dry paper, finally leaving a perfectly smooth surface for painting

*Right:* the area to be sprayed should be masked from the rest of the car, using paper and tape. Primer should be applied before turning attention to the top coat

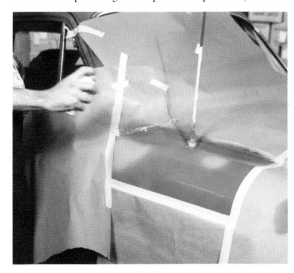

OWING TO A NUMBER of factors, including the soaring cost of skilled labour and constant increases in the price of spare body parts, perhaps the most expensive repairs carried out on the average motor car are those concerned with bodywork damage. These high costs and, in some cases, a low standard of finished work, are encouraging more and more private motorists to attempt to repair minor body damage themselves. This can, in many cases, be carried out quite successfully by a reasonably competent do-it-yourself man but it must be borne in mind that a modicum of skill, a lot of patience and considerable time must be spent on carrying out such work if a high standard of finish is to be achieved.

Furthermore, no attempt at rectifying body damage should be made unless a thorough study of the cause and effect of the incident responsible for the damage is carried out. Although body damage may appear to be only superficial to the untrained eye, a creased panel or a slightly buckled wing may hide a much more serious condition which is inherently dangerous to the performance and safety of the vehicle.

If a car has received what appears to be superficial damage to the front or front wing areas, a careful inspection should be made to ensure that the radiator has not been punctured or moved. Following this a careful check should be made on the water level at every opportunity to ensure that water is not leaking away through a badly fitting or stretched hose or from a damaged coupling. If the vehicle in question is fitted with a water temperature gauge this too should be checked; first of all to make sure tht it is still in working order and then a watch should be kept on it to ascertain whether the cooling system is still functioning at the same level of efficiency as before the incident causing the damage.

Yet another check may be instituted by inspecting the headlamp settings. If it proves impossible, or even

When using resin, only a small amount should be mixed with hardener at a time, otherwise it may dry before it is needed. A plastic cup is ideal for mixing the two components, which should be stirred thoroughly. To fill a split in a metal panel, resin should be applied to the back of the split, after the surface has been thoroughly cleaned and derusted. Plastic tape should be stuck to the front of the split, to prevent the resin running through

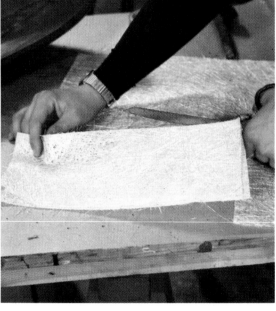

A suitable grade and size of glassfibre matting should be chosen—the patch should generously cover the split. It pays to wear plastic or rubber gloves when dealing with glassfibre, as it tends to stick in the skin. The matting should be laid on the resin, then more resin should be worked into the matting, using a stippling brush, until the glassfibre is totally impregnated. This should then be allowed to dry

It is advisable to lay up a second piece of matting on the first, after it has dried, to give it added strength. The same procedure should be followed. When this is dry, the tape can be removed from the front of the split and the indentation filled using a paste mix worked carefully into the damaged area. When mixing filler, do so by 'layering' as stirring tends to introduce air bubbles which need refilling after rubbing down

just very difficult to set these correctly following what appears to have been a minor accident, this could indicate something quite serious, such as a twisted subframe or a deformed side rail in the vehicle's unitary body.

A careful study should also be made of the steering performance of the vehicle following minor shunts. If the steering should develop a distinct pull to one side, or be unable to hold a straight line when the driver removes his hands from the steering wheel, this usually indicates that some damage has been caused to the steering linkage or that the steering geometry of the car has been affected. Furthermore, the braking action of the car should still ensure that it pulls up in a straight line when the brakes are applied. Another check should be made for uneven tyre wear on one or both front wheels. If the steering geometry has been affected in any way, uneven wear should quickly manifest itself and the services of a proper garage be used to return the whole steering system to peak efficiency.

Other indicators that serious though hidden damage has occurred, include a badly fitting bonnet lid or passenger doors that do not shut without extra effort being applied or which, suddenly, do not match up with the door striker plates on the door pillars.

A similar check should be carried out following damage to the rear section of the car. The boot lid should be checked for ease of action and tight fit. Uneven tyre wear should be watched for on the rear wheels also. A simple method of testing the rear-wheel geometry and brakes is to use only the handbrake to pull up the vehicle on a deserted stretch of road. As the modern car's handbrake usually works only on the rear wheels, any pulling to one side by the vehicle would indicate that a more thorough check should be made on the whole rear suspension and braking system.

Rust is another factor that should be considered when discussing body damage. Any rust appearing on the surface of a motor car's bodywork should be dealt with immediately by sanding away and then repainting with primer and a matching proprietary paint.

Body damage is not dealt with quite so easily, even though repairs are within the capability of most people, provided sufficient time and care is taken at each stage of the repair procedure. The equipment needed consists, usually, of an electric power hand tool, a body file, some sheets of rubbing down paper of various grades, a rubbing block, a screwdriver and a proprietary body filler kit which contains both the filler compound and a catalytic agent. For finishing the repair the usual method is to use aerosol cans of primer and paint, readily available from most accessory shops.

It can be deduced from the above, that amateur body repairs do not involve the body straightening or panel beating techniques used by the professional. The main method for the amateur is to use the body filler to restore the original contour of the damaged panel and to repaint it, rather than to attempt to restore the damaged metal to its original condition.

The first step in a repair of this nature is to fit a coarse sanding disc to the power tool and use this to sand away paint, primer, dirt and rust from the damaged area until bare metal is showing. Care should be taken to sand right to the edges of the area under repair and just slightly into the surrounding, undamaged paintwork. After power sanding a medium grade of rubbing paper should be fitted to the rubbing block and used on the metal to give a high degree of smoothness to the affected area. Touching the sanded area with the fingertips should be avoided as grease from the skin will prevent the filler compound from 'keying' properly to the prepared area and could result in an unsatisfactory standard of finish.

The next stage is to prepare the filler compound. A quantity of paste (perhaps half a small can, but dependent on the size of the area to be repaired) should be scooped out of the can and placed on a clean, smooth working surface which is free from pitting or ridging—a piece of Formica is ideal. The paste should be spread out and the catalytic agent—which converts the paste into a hard setting, very tough and durable compound—is added to the paste. The usual proportion is a half tube of the catalyst to a half can of paste.

Using the paste applicator, usually a piece of stiff plastic which is included in the filler kit, mix the paste and the catalyst with a smooth forwards and backwards action of the wrist. This should be done in such a manner as to ensure that not only are the two parts of the compound mixed thoroughly, but also that any air bubbles trapped in the filler are eliminated.

Again using the applicator, apply the filler to the damaged area of the car, just a little at a time and spread in layers. Pushing the filler hard down onto the area, layers should be applied until the filler stands a little proud of the remainder of the body panel under

repair. The filler should then be allowed to harden. Time taken for this varies and heat can be used to accelerate the process, but the longer a car can be left in a clean, dry atmosphere the better. Even so, two or three days is more than sufficient.

Once the filler has set, the high spots of it should be rubbed away. The first step in this process is undertaken with the special, but inexpensive body file which can be adjusted to conform to the curvature of the vehicle's contours. Following this, a medium grade of rubbing paper fitted to the rubbing block should be used to smooth the repaired area and to feather the repair into the surrounding, undamaged areas of the vehicle's bodywork.

Once a smooth finish has been achieved—and in order to effect a really first class job—the repair should be left for at least a week, preferably two. After this, a final skim coat of the body filler is applied to the area after sanding down once more with a fine grade of wet or dry paper and then drying off thoroughly. The skim coat should be so thin as to allow the original filler to be seen through it and the purpose of this final coat is to fill in any small and in some cases invisible holes which might have appeared on the original surface.

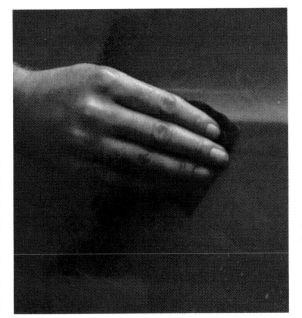

*Left:* before repairing a scratch, clean the surrounding area with a cloth dipped in white spirit. This will remove any grease or wax which might prevent filler from 'keying' into the damaged part

*Right:* mix a small quantity of filler paste and rub it across the scratch so that it completely fills the depression. Leave the filler standing slightly proud so that it can be rubbed smooth when dry. Use only a very fine grade of wet-or-dry paper and keep it wet

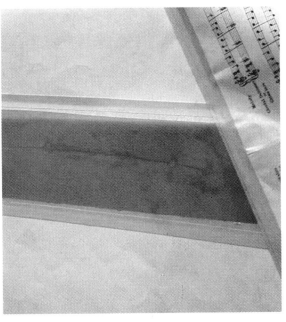

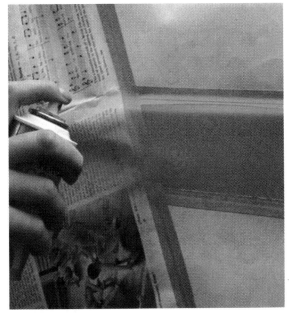

*Left:* once the surface of the filler is flush with the existing paint, mask the area surrounding the damage from the rest of the body, using newspaper and masking tape. Make sure the surface is dry before painting

*Right:* apply two coats of primer before turning to the top coat. Once again, use wet-or-dry paper to smooth the paint between coats. Keep spraying top coats until the area is completely covered and shows no patches

Following this, and having allowed time for the skim to harden, the whole area should be rubbed down once more with a very fine grade of rubbing paper, used dry, and then finally finished off with an even finer grade of wet or dry paper, used wet and without the rubbing block, using light hand pressure only.

After allowing this final skim coat to harden thoroughly, perhaps for another week, the repair is then ready for painting. To do this, the area to be painted should be washed thoroughly with clean, cold water and then dried. Brown paper and adhesive tape should then be used to mask around the repaired area in order to prevent overspray affecting undamaged paintwork. If working in the wing area of the car the wheels and tyres should also be masked off; and if working near glass this too should be covered over.

Aerosol primer is then applied, the aerosol being held about 12 inches from the area to be sprayed and a forward and backward action is used, taking care to spray in a straight line and not with an arcing action. Allow the primer to dry and then rub down with a very fine grade of wet or dry paper, used wet. Wash the primed area and then allow to dry thoroughly. Paint should be applied in the same way as the primer but with the button of the aerosol being released at the end of each stroke in order to minimise paint build up.

A further coat of paint should be applied once the original layer has been allowed to dry thoroughly, the method being the same as before. Once the final coat has been applied, it should be allowed to dry for around three to four weeks. After this period, the surface of the repaired area should be rubbed down with a special compounding paste, again freely available from most good accessory shops. By taking care at this stage, the paint will be gradually polished to an acceptable level and, if all the steps taken have been performed correctly, the repaired area of the bodywork should be undistinguishable from other areas of the car.    TN

*Right:* because steel wheels are subject to rust it may become necessary to repaint them. They should first be rubbed down with a suitable wet-or-dry paper, depending upon the amount of rust, before applying a primer. It is advisable to check wheels every so often as rust and neglect can lead to weakened and damaged wheel nuts and rims

*Right:* after rubbing the wheels down, an aerosol primer should be applied and left to dry. The primer aerosol should be held about twelve inches from the area to be sprayed and moved in a forwards and backwards motion. Following this, the primed surface should again be rubbed down before a final coat of paint is applied

# A FAMILY OF INNOVATORS
## Three pioneers of the motoring age

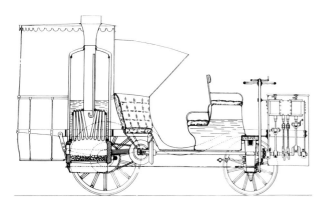 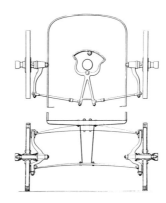

Side and plan views of Amédée senior's La Mancelle, of 1878. This was a six-seater steam carriage, available with either *calèche* or *postchaise* bodywork, and was powered by a front-mounted, vertical-twin-cylinder engine—probably the first bonneted, front-engined vehicle. The main feature, which was years ahead of its time, was the independent suspension

**Amédée Bollée snr 1844–1917**

IN THE ESOTERIC CRAFT of bell-founding, the name of Bollée of Le Mans is one of great renown. Yet the Bollée whose technical skills in this sphere were probably most famous is almost certainly better known for his achievements in pioneering the self-propelled road vehicle, a field in which his two sons were at least his equal.

Amédée Bollée senior was born in 1844; in 1867 he visited the Paris World Exhibition and saw for the first time the new Michaux velocipede and steam omnibuses. This inspired him to develop a 'fast private carriage', and in 1871 he established a workshop within the family foundry. In the short space of two years, he developed a machine of quite revolutionary design, which combined many features of vehicles produced nearly a century later.

His steam carriage, L'Obéissante, broke completely with the traditions of horse vehicle design and railway engineering which had characterised earlier road vehicles. It had a 12-seater body panelled in metal with embossed 'quilted' patterning and the rivetted iron chassis swept up into arches above the iron-spoked wheels; the front pair being carried in independently-sprung forks. Steering, by twin chains running over elliptical cams, was geometrically precise—in complete contrast to the centre-pivot cart steering used on many Victorian steam carriages—and controlled from a central steering wheel. Each rear wheel was driven by a separate V-twin engine, and the steering could be aided by shutting off the steam supply to one engine or the other, allowing L'Obéissante to pivot about the stationary rear wheel.

Tests proved the vehicle so successful that the Minister of Public Works granted permission for its use over a specified area, provided that the district engineer was given three days' warning of the itinerary which would be followed. In 1875,

Bollée drove his carriage to Paris, where it enjoyed a *succès d'éstime*, despite having broken 75 traffic laws on the journey. This general layout was followed by Bollée's next venture, two four-wheel-driven, four-wheel-steered, all-round-independently-sprung tramcars with steam power assistance for clutch and steering.

But neither L'Obéissante nor the trams proved commercially successful, and Bollée turned to a new layout for his next vehicle, La Mancelle of 1878.

This was probably the first vehicle to have the engine at the front under a bonnet, driving the rear axle through a propeller shaft, bevel gears and side chains; it lacked only a gearbox to predate the Système Panhard invented in 1892 by Emile Levassor. La Mancelle had independent suspension by transverse leaf springs, a layout that would not reappear until well into the petrol age.

Bollée showed La Mancelle at the 1878 Paris World Exhibition. He received orders which encouraged him to appoint a *concessionaire general*, one M. Lecordier, and to establish a workshop outside the factory. Replicas of La Mancelle, with either *calèche* or *postchaise* bodywork, were offered and at least one was built; so, too, were two larger tractors built on the same lines, but with the added feature of a power take-off which drove the wheels of the tender. A rich Berlin banker named Barthold Aerons acquired the rights to produce the design in Germany. He had a grandiose plan to set up public bus services in Germany, Austria, Russia and Sweden, but the scheme was far too ambitious. Though twenty-two vehicles were built for Aerons in the Wöhlert factory, in 1883 the company collapsed, the banker was ruined and Bollée received none of the royalty payments that had been due to him.

In 1880, Bollée built a new closed carriage, La

**Amédée Bollée jnr 1868–1926**

**Léon Bollée 1870–1913**

Nouvelle, for his father; it was probably the first saloon car ever, and was still capable of competing with honour in the Paris-Bordeaux-Paris race of 1895.

But Amédée Bollée was losing interest in steam carriage production, which had cost him a small fortune, and he abandoned his ambition of perfecting a perfect road vehicle. In 1881, however, he built a remarkable six-seater, La Rapide, for his brother. Capable of 37 mph on solid iron tyres, this final model (of which two examples were produced) could be stoked and driven by one man.

From then on, Amédée Bollée devoted his life (he died in 1917) to bell-founding, and when the Marquis de Brox asked him, in 1886, to build a steam carriage, he passed the commission over to his 18-year-old elder son, also called Amédée.

Amédée Bollée jnr had already built for himself a light two-seater steamer of advance concept. The vast machine he designed for the Marquis was a 16-seater 'double mail coach' which appeared as archaic as the two-seater was ahead of its time. But, it is for his petrol vehicles that Amédée Bollée jnr is remembered, although it was not until 1896 that his first successful petrol car appeared.

This had a 2.3-litre, twin-cylinder engine, cast *en bloc*, mounted at the front of a metal chassis. Belt primary drive transmitted power to a Panhard-type gearbox, from which a transverse countershaft, incorporating a differential, drove each rear wheel through separate longitudinal propeller shafts with spiral bevel gearing at either end. This was the first time that spiral bevels had been used in a car transmission, but the arrangement was soon abandoned for side chains. The car was built under licence by De Dietrich; an early modification was the fitting of an automatic spray carburettor of sophisticated design.

Amédée Bollée jnr took part in a number of speed trials, as a result of which it became apparent to him that an attempt to reduce the air-resistance of the average motor car body was essential. He secretly prepared four 8 hp racing cars, with bodywork made entirely of aluminium, aggressively pointed at front and rear to give a smooth passage to the air; these *torpilleurs*, capable of a 'breakneck' 37 mph, were described by *L'Express* of Liège as 'fearsome but speedy'.

In the 1898 Paris-Amsterdam race, the four *torpilleurs* attracted much attention. Two of the cars, including that driven by Bollée jnr himself, were eliminated *en route*, but the others, driven by Gaudry and Loysel, were third and sixth. Gaudry might have been higher placed but for a 'bad spill' on the Etain road. Vinet, though out of the race, concluded an excellent stroke of business by selling his car at Monter for the useful sum of 17,000 francs!

Orders for touring versions of the new Bollée model poured in following the Paris–Amsterdam race—De Dietrich booked orders exceeding one million francs within a few weeks.

Towards the end of 1898, Loysel, driving his Paris–Amsterdam racer, won the Bordeaux–Biarritz race, while Thévin and Houry succeeded in driving Bollée-Dietrich tourers from Paris to St Petersburg and back.

Around the same time, the 'engineer-explorer', Taupeat de Saint-Symeux, was the first automobilist to reach the Niger, linking the valley of

*Top Left:* L'Obeissante, built in 1873, was a 12-seater steam-driven coach that had separate V-engines driving each wheel independently. On its first journey, to Paris, in 1875, it broke 75 traffic laws!

*Centre far left:* Amédée jnr's first car was a light, 2-seater steamer, built in 1885

*Centre left:* the 1901 Tourer was based on the 1899 Torpilleurs that competed in the Tour De France. The Tourers had 4-cylinder, twin-carburettor engines that enabled them to attain speeds in excess of 22 mph

*Bottom left:* Amédée jnr's last car, the Type-F, was built from 1913 to 1919. He then turned to the manufacture of piston rings

*Right:* the luxurious 'Double Berline' of 1911

*Below left:* the Leon Bollée Landaulet 25/30 hp of 1910

*Below right:* the Léon Bollée Torpedo of 1912

Senegal with Bamako on a Bollée; in 1899, he was the second motorist to reach Tananarive by car, and the first to make the journey without dismounting from his machine.

The most important speed event was the 1350-mile Tour de France organised by *Le Matin*; for this race, Amédée Bollée jnr designed three new torpilleurs with a precocious mechanical layout which included an incredible number of 'firsts'.

The cars had rear-mounted, 20 hp, four-cylinder engines cast *en bloc* and fitted with twin carburettors, a boxed-up steel chassis, of unusual strength, independently suspended at the front (on double transverse springs, of course) and underslung at the rear, twin track rods and aluminium coachwork which was not only smoothly streamlined above the chassis but also flat underneath to lessen air resistance. There were, however, some archaic features—four-speed belt-drive, automatic inlet valves and hot-tube ignition. Hasty preparation spoiled the cars' chances, and road dust, sucked in by the carburettors, caused pre-ignition which was a major factor in the team's withdrawal, though the cars showed themselves capable of 55 mph on the road.

This fiasco marked Bollée's withdrawal from competition motoring. Henceforth, he was to concentrate on limited-production cars of great refinement. One 1902 project had a twin-cylinder engine with a vibration damper consisting of a third piston running counter to the others in an open-ended cylinder.

In 1907, came the Type E, possibly the world's first ergonomically-designed motor car, priced at the same level as, and far more advanced in concept than, a Rolls-Royce Silver Ghost. The mechanical refinement of this model was further enhanced by the adoption of another Bollée invention, hydraulic tappets. In 1908, Bollée played host to the Wright Brothers when they gave their first European displays of flying.

The last production Amédée Bollée car was the Type F of 1913; when the last of these had been assembled from pre-war spares in 1919, Bollée turned his attention to the manufacture of piston rings, in which field his factory is still active. He died in 1926.

His younger brother, Léon, born in 1870, invented a remarkable calculating machine, which was shown at the 1889 Paris Exhibition; until he was twenty-six he involved himself with the design of automatic machinery. Then, early in 1896, he conceived a small, fast three-wheeler of somewhat basic design, remarkable mainly for the fact that it was the first vehicle to be sold with pneumatic tyres as standard. 'The elongated form of the tricycle, redolent of speed,' wrote Baudry de Saunier in 1896, 'gives it somewhat the semblance of a little torpedo-boat.' The machine was built under licence in France and England.

English rights were acquired by the egregious Harry Lawson for £20,000 and a crude version of the machine, known as the Coventry Motette, was produced. However, the Bollée voiturette was only a short-lived venture. By 1899, Darracq were producing a new Léon Bollée, inspired partly by the voiturette layout.

After 1903, Léon Bollée turned to manufacture on his own account, building large conventional cars backed by Vanderbilt money; he died in 1913 and the subsequent products of his factory were indistinguishable from most other middle-class French cars of the 1920s. In 1924, the factory was acquired by William Morris, who produced mainly Wolseley-inspired models at Le Mans for seven years, until the Depression caused him to sell the works, which closed in 1933.   DBW

# Motor Racing's Diplomat

Bonnier at work in his own Lola T280 3-litre sports car, during the 1972 Le Mans 24-hour race. Early on Sunday morning, the car left the track and Bonnier was killed

JOAKIM BONNIER, who was killed during the 1972 Le Mans 24-Hour race, had a long and distinguished motor-racing career which reached its zenith in 1959 when he joined the BRM Formula One team and won the Dutch Grand Prix for them. Bonnier was one of the first Swedes to tackle motor racing seriously in the post-war years and led the way for other Swedish drivers like Ronnie Peterson and Reine Wisell.

Bonnier was born in Stockholm in 1930, the son of a professor who ensured that his son had an international education in Paris and Oxford before taking up employment with his uncle's publishing business. However, like so many young men born into a comfortable way of life, he forsook it and first of all spent three years in the Swedish Navy as a lieutenant, before taking up motor racing seriously. He had, in fact, been taking part in rallies since he was eighteen, specialising in the type of rough-road rallies at which the Scandinavians excel.

He also took part in ice racing using Citroën and Alfa Romeo cars, and it was his success with Alfa Romeo that prompted the Italian company to ask him to distribute their cars in Sweden. This naturally gave him access to the best competition cars from the Italian firm and he used a 3½-litre Disco Volante Alfa Romeo to good effect, winning the 1955 Stockholm Grand Prix. He also made his debut in England that year, taking the Disco Volante to a fine victory at Oulton Park, and this victory did much to bring his name to the attention of the British racing teams.

In 1956, he became a full-time professional, running a privately owned 1½-litre Maserati in international events, albeit with little success. He was then taken into the Maserati sports-car team for 1957 and in 1958 joined the Maserati Formula One team, driving the 2½-litre 250F. Unfortunately, this was the year that Britain's Vanwall team swept all before them and his only successes were in the Naples GP and the non-Championship United States GP.

For 1959, Bonnier was invited to join the hitherto unsuccessful BRM team and promptly won for them the 1959 Dutch Grand Prix, a race which was also remarkable for the fact that every one of the starters finished the race and not a single pit stop was made. The Dutch victory was a flash in the pan for BRM, however: although

Bonnier stayed with them in 1960, he never finished a race in a higher position than fifth. In sports-car racing he was driving for Porsche and, as well as enjoying several minor wins, he co-drove the winning Porsche with Hans Herrmann in the 1960 Targa Florio race.

He raced the Porsche 1½-litre Formula One car in 1961 and 1962, but the car was not fast enough, although he collected several third places.

By the early '60s, it had become evident that Bonnier did not have the qualities to become World Champion, for he lacked the sheer speed to win Formula One races; in sports-car racing, though, he was much in demand for long distance events.

From 1963 to 1965, Bonnier drove for the Rob Walker private team in Formula One races, first with a Cooper and later with a Brabham. His best placings in either of these cars were fifth places at Monaco, Spa and Mexico. However, in sports-car racing he continued to excel, winning the 1963 Targa Florio and the 1964 Reims 12-Hour race with Graham Hill for Ferrari. He was second at Le Mans in 1964, again with Graham Hill, in a 330P Ferrari, and won the Paris 1000 Kilometre race at Montlhéry, also with a Ferrari.

When Formula One changed to 3-litres in 1966, Bonnier was obliged to buy his own car to remain in top-class motor racing. He purchased a Cooper-Maserati, which was uncompetitive even in faster hands than Bonnier's, and his best placing in 1966 was sixth at Mexico. The following year he scored a fifth place in the German Grand Prix and sixth in the United States GP. His sports-car prowess remained, however, and he drove the American Chaparral in 1966, winning the Nürburgring 1000 km race, with Phil Hill as his co-driver.

For 1968, he tried a Formula One McLaren-BRM, but had little success during the year, apart from 6th place at the Italian GP. He was given a drive in the Honda V12 F1 car at Mexico that year, where he finished sixth.

He purchased a Lotus 49 for the 1969 season and looked forward to a more successful year, but crashed the car at Oulton Park and never raced it again. He switched to a McLaren M7C for Formula One, but by 1970, at the age of 40, he was not at all competitive against younger men in newer machinery and he wisely retired from single-seater racing that year, making the grand gesture of hanging his McLaren on the sitting room wall of his home in Lausanne, Switzerland, where he ran an art gallery.

Like so many drivers before him, he could not forsake the wheel, so he switched to the new 2-litre European Sports Car Championship with a Lola, and on many occasions showed younger men that his skill had not gone, by notching up victories at several European tracks.

For 1972, he purchased two of the new 3-litre Lola T280 sports cars with which he planned to tackle the World Sports Car Championship. The cars proved to be very fast, but rather fragile and ill maintained. He managed to win the mini-Le Mans four-hour race in 1972 and led in the early stages of the 24-Hour race. He dropped to eighth in the early hours of Sunday morning, but started to make up time rapidly after a pit stop with brake problems. He was lapping a Ferrari Daytona, when the two cars collided and the tiny Lola shot over the safety barrier into the trees lining the track at Indianapolis corner. Bonnier was killed instantly.

Bonnier's main claim to a place in the history of motor racing is not for his racing record, excellent though it was, but for his ability as an international diplomat, pleading the cause of motor racing safety and advancing the image of Grand Prix drivers from that of glorified playboys to international stars. He founded the Grand Prix Drivers' Association, in 1962, and was its chairman until he died, leading the fight for drivers' rights. With his fluent command of six languages and aristocratic bearing, emphasised by his neat beard, he added a lustre to the sport of motor racing. Joakim Bonnier will never be replaced.

NB

# An exceedingly pleasant rival

*Left:* Pietro Bordino in the car that he raced in the 1922 Italian Grand Prix to lead home a Fiat 1–2–3–4. *Right:* Bordino and his mechanic Felice Nazzaro in the supercharged 1½-litre Fiat on the 1924 Targa Florio. Note how they lean into the corner, motor-cycle fashion

PIETRO BORDINO, probably the finest road-racing driver of his generation, was born in Italy in 1890. In 1904, he was acting as riding mechanic in Fiat racers, accompanying Felice Nazzaro, Vincente Lancia and Ralph DePalma. By 1908 he had become a competition driver himself, making his debut at the Chateau-Thierry hill-climb. In 1911, he went to England with the giant four-cylinder, 28-litre 300 bhp Fiat racer, which made a number of high-speed runs at Brooklands. His career did not start in earnest, however, until 1921, when his twin-ohc Fiat took the lead at the start of the 1921 Brescia Grand Prix and kept it until the fourteenth lap; first tyre troubles and then a broken oil pipe caused his retirement. As it was his first appearance in an international event, Bordino's performance—which included a record lap speed of 96.3 mph—was doubly remarkable.

Already he had established a reputation as a driver whose methods were of a type likely to endear him to every enthusiast who met him, since he believed most firmly in getting the absolute maximum from his car whether it would last or not.

These were the characteristics which marked his performance in the 1922 French Grand Prix at Strasbourg: he left his two team-mates, the veteran Felice Nazzaro and his nephew Biagio, far behind, leading from the second lap. Valve-stem trouble eliminated his principal rivals, the Sunbeams, and it looked as though the race would be a walkover for Bordino, when two laps from the end his back axle fractured. This was a fault common to all three team cars and had already cost the life, earlier in the race, of young Biagio Nazzaro, although Felice Nazzaro's car lasted the distance to win.

The opening of the new Monza Autodrome in September 1922, provided Bordino with two sensational victories, the first in the 373-mile Voiturette Grand Prix, in which he led a 1–2–3–4 Fiat victory at a speed of 83.25 mph, followed a week later by a clear-cut victory in the first European Grand Prix, his winning speed being 86.90 mph, with a fastest lap of 91.3 mph.

'No man could handle a racing machine better at high speed on really tricky corners', said *Autocar*. On the twisting Tours circuit used for the 1923 French GP, Bordino justified that statement by setting up the fastest lap (85.6 mph) in practice, eclipsed this in a shattering burst of speed with an 87.18 mph opening lap and led for the first eight laps until the supercharger on his Fiat swallowed flying stones and choked.

The European GP at Monza brought deeper disappointment: a stub-axle broke in Bordino's car during practice, killing his passenger, Giaccone, and injuring Bordino to such an extent that his new mechanic had to shift gears for him during the race. Even so, he led for more than half the distance, until a violent skid, caused by the loss of a rear tyre tread, prompted him to retire.

He opened the 1924 season with fourth place in the Targa Florio, even though his little 1½–litre supercharged Fiat was quite the wrong car for the Madonie circuit. He fainted on the fourth lap and Nazzaro had to finish the race for him.

He soon went into the lead in the 1924 French Grand Prix at Lyon, and put up a magnificent performance until brake failure put his car out.

It was the high point of his career. He managed tenth place at Indianapolis in 1925, but the new 1926–7 1½-litre GP formula was not to his liking, and he made few appearances, although he won the 1927 GP of Milan at Monza with the new type 806 V12 Fiat. Soon after this, Fiat finally withdrew from racing.

Bordino changed to a Type 35 Bugatti, with which he took seventh place in the three-litre class of the 1928 Mille Miglia, but shortly afterwards, while practising on the Targa Florio circuit in Italy, he collided with a large dog, which jammed the steering, causing him to crash fatally.

'Not only was he a fine driver, he was an exceedingly pleasant rival,' recalled his obituary in *Autocar*. Only a few days after Bordino's death the first Coppa Pietro Bordino race was run over the Allesandria circuit.

This turned out to be the first major victory for the driver who was to replace Bordino in the affection of Italian motor racing fans—Tazio Nuvolari.                    DBW

# A SOPHISTICATED FAILURE

Borgward technical specifications were impressive, but sales were not good enough, so its short life came to an end

CARL F. BORGWARD was an acquisitive German automobile engineer who, before World War II, purchased the Hansa, Hansa-Lloyd and Goliath factories. He turned out a variety of small cars before the war, his best known being the four-cylinder, ohv Hansa 1100, which was built from 1934 to 1939. This model was supplemented by the 1700, which was simply the 1100 with two further cylinders added. This 40 bhp car was capable of 65 mph and featured independent suspension on all wheels. There was even a sport version of the car which had its power output improved to 50 bhp. Engine size of the Hansa range gradually crept upwards to two litres and, just before the war, Borgward unveiled a special version of the two-litre six, with twin overhead camshafts, which produced a high power output for the time. The onset of the War prevented any further developments and the Borgward factories, centred mostly on Bremen, were put to war work.

After the war, Borgward got back into their stride earlier than most German car makers and announced the Hansa 1500 at the 1949 Geneva Show. This was an advanced and attractive car with all enveloping

*Far left:* the Borgward Hansa 1500, of 1949, had a 48 bhp, 1.5-litre engine and a top speed of 75 mph

*Above and left:* the Borgward 2000 of 1939, powered by a straight six engine. Note the transverse leaf spring

*Below:* the 1954 Isabella saloon

bodywork, which was powered by a four-cylinder, ohv engine giving 52 bhp and a top speed of 75 mph. Borgward was a staunch believer in the publicity value of competition and, in 1950, a streamlined version of the car with a 66 bhp engine took twelve international class speed records at Montlhéry, including 1000 miles at an average of 107.3 mph.

The cars were renamed Borgward soon afterwards, although various Lloyd and Goliath models were also made, mostly to cater for the bubble car boom of the late fifties. The most popular Borgward was the Isabella, which was developed from the earlier Hansa and announced in 1954. This attractive car soon gained a following among the knowledgeable motorists of Europe for it was a 90 mph saloon with seating capacity for five passengers and independent suspension on all wheels. The Isabella was used in saloon-car racing by drivers all over the world, but nowhere to better effect than in Britain where the Dutch/Norwegian driver Bill Blydenstein took his Isabella to countless victories.

The Borgward factory embarked on an ambitious competition programme, but, instead of using their experimental twin-overhead-camshaft, 1500 cc, four-cylinder engine, they used a modified pushrod engine. In 1952, Hans Hugo Hartmann gained victories at the Grenzlandring and Avus circuits in his Borgward RS with the pushrod engine, which now gave 100 bhp. A fuel-injected unit, based on the Isabella engine, was being used by 1954, still with the same bore and stroke as the basic Isabella block. This engine, which produced 115 bhp, was good enough to give Bechem victory in the 1954 Eifelrennen at the Nürburgring. In 1955, the car gained a class victory in the Mille Miglia, and, for 1956, an entirely new racing engine was devised.

This new engine still had the same 84.5 mm bore and 75 mm stroke of the 1488 cc Isabella, but the

*Above:* the Isabella TS coupé had a 1493 cc, 75 bhp engine and a top speed of almost 100 mph. Some thought this car very pretty, while others found it cluttered

*Below:* despite its good looks and brisk performance, the Isabella could not stop the company folding

*Bottom:* in a last effort, to stay afloat, in 1960, Borgward produced a 6-cylinder, 100 bhp luxury limousine with air-suspension

engine had a Silumin (silicon-aluminium) block, wet liners and a new twin-overhead-camshaft cylinder head with four valves per cylinder. It also featured fuel injection, dry-sump lubrication and twin ignition systems. The sturdy engine had a five-bearing crankshaft with chain drive to the camshafts and, on a 10.2:1 compression ratio, it gave 150 bhp at 7500 rpm.

The car had little success in its first two seasons, although Hans Herrmann did gain second place in the European Mountain Championship in 1957. The tiny open Borgward RS was often out of luck in circuit racing, but when Jo Bonnier joined the team, in 1958, he gave the all-conquering 1500 cc Porsches a run for their money in the German sports-car championship. Bonnier lost first place at the Avus by only 0.8 sec and Borgward had to be content with second place in the championship. Bonnier also had to be content with second place in the European Mountain Championship, but he won the important Freiburg hill-climb by a very big margin.

On the production side, the Isabella continued throughout the '50s, supplemented by the pretty TS coupé, but sales could never quite keep the company far enough ahead of their creditors and, in 1960, the smaller Lloyd Arabella was given the Borgward name in an effort to boost sales of this cheaper car.

Borgward retired from racing in 1958, not from choice but because of financial problems. However, the twin-cam racing engine was lent to private owners, to fit into single-seater chassis, most notably Stirling Moss who raced a Cooper in the 1½-litre Formula Two with this engine. The engine gave around 175 bhp by this time and Moss was able to gain some success with it. Even later, when Formula One went to 1½-litres in 1961, the German driver Kuhnke attempted to use the engine in Formula One racing, albeit with no success at all.

In a last gesture to grab a share of the luxury market, Borgward announced a limousine, a large car powered by a 100 bhp, six-cylinder engine. It had optional air suspension and many other luxury touches, but it failed to attract much attention and only ten months later, in 1961, the Borgward company succumbed to its financial difficulties, once and for all, and was closed down.

There was much rumour of Britain's BMC taking over the Bremen factories for the expansion of Austin and Morris sales in Europe, but negotiations fell through. A small German firm bought up enough stocks of parts to sell cars for a few years and a Mexican firm, Fanasa, purchased the tooling from Bremen with the idea of building Isabellas under licence in Mexico. These schemes never seemed to get off the ground, and as far as serious production was concerned the Borgward company died in 1961. MT

# The quiet champion

Jack Brabham, the constructor, seen here testing the 1966 F3 BT21 at Goodwood

JOHN ARTHUR BRABHAM was the man who began the invasion of Grand Prix racing by the men from 'Down Under'. Although Australians and New Zealanders had raced in Europe before, he was the man who put Australia on the international motor racing map and, by his example, encouraged drivers like Bruce McLaren and Denny Hulme and talented designers like Ron Tauranac and Ralph Bellamy to throw up their lives in the Antipodes for the risky profession of racing driver or mechanic in Europe.

Born in Sydney in 1926, Jack Brabham was the son of a greengrocer whose father had emigrated to Australia from London's East End in 1885. Although there was no family background in engineering or competition motoring, the young Brabham soon became involved in cycling, motor-cycling and cars. He did best at technical subjects in school and when he left school, at 15, he went into a garage to learn the trade. He was called up for the Australian Air Force towards the end of World War II and spent a couple of years repairing Beaufighters.

When he was demobbed from the RAAF, in 1946, he had a workshop built at his grandfather's house and began to service and maintain cars from the neighbourhood. He might still have been there but for the arrival in Hurstville of an American, Johnny Schonberg, who had married a local girl. Brabham and Schonberg became friendly and one day the American invited Brabham to join him on an expedition to Darwin to buy war surplus trucks. On the way there, they had to stop in Brisbane. Schonberg took Brabham to a speedway track where midget cars raced. Schonberg was quite a star driver at the Sydney track, but Brabham had never gone to watch. Interested by the spectacle of these tiny cars broadsiding their way round the cinder covered $\frac{1}{4}$-mile oval, Brabham soon became a regular spectator back at the Sydney track and before long, he decided that he could build a better car than the one Schonberg was racing. Using parts from a Morris Cowley, an Amilcar, and a Harley-Davidson motor cycle, Brabham built up a car powered by an 1100 cc JAP twin-

cylinder engine. The engine proved unreliable so he built up a new 1350 cc engine, making most of the engine parts himself. This engine was very powerful and Schonberg went through a successful season before his wife began to complain about his dangerous hobby. Up to this time, Brabham had given little thought to the possibility of driving as the engineering challenge was more interesting to him at that time. However, Schonberg offered him a drive in the car when he retired, and after a few lessons on some nearby mud flats Brabham was taken to the Paramatta Speedway and entered for his first race.

There was no storybook beginning to the Brabham career—he finished dead last in his first race, and the next, and the one after that. But after nights of eating the cinders thrown up by the other cars he was beginning to get the hang of driving the midget and when, on the third night, he was started from the front row of the grid, with the best drivers right at the back, he stayed in front to notch up his first victory.

For the 1963 season, Brabham raced the BT7, which had a Coventry-Climax 1½-litre V8. Despite engine problems, the car had a fairly successful season

Once he had acquired the taste of winning he became almost unbeatable. He won the New South Wales Championship in his first season and he carried on for six more years as a professional midget racer, until one night in Adelaide the venerable JAP engine blew itself to pieces and he decided he'd had enough of midget racing.

Brabham was almost lost to motor racing at that point: he nearly joined his father in the greengrocery business, but by then he had met Ron Tauranac, who was later to become the chief designer of Brabham cars. Tauranac was involved in hill-climbing, a strictly amateur sport, and Brabham became interested. He used the midget in a hill-climb and was far faster than most of the opposition, so he turned to the sport seriously, changing the midget for a Mk. IV Cooper 500 and then a Mk. V Cooper with a 1000 cc Vincent HRD engine. By this time, Brabham had married Betty, who was, fortunately, a motor racing fan.

Brabham's first step on the road to fame in road racing came when a Cooper-Bristol was put up for sale in Australia. This front-engined car was considered quite a 'hot' machine in Australia and he was able to buy the new car at a good price when the original purchaser committed suicide

before taking delivery. He had obtained sponsorship from Redex for the car, which was to be called the Redex Special, but Australia's ruling body, the Confederation of Australian Motor Sports, had ruled that advertising would not be permitted so the aggrieved Brabham took his car off to New Zealand in 1954 where he raced in the New Zealand Grand Prix and met some of the international stars for the first time. He finished sixth in the race and his appetite was whetted.

Jack spent some time racing the Cooper-Bristol in Australia and New Zealand, winning at most of the major circuits and getting his name known. He took part in the 1955 New Zealand GP, finishing fourth, but more important he met Dean Delamont, the Competitions Director of the RAC. Delamont impressed the young Brabham with his stories of racing in Europe and suggested that Brabham come to England and try his hand at 'real' motor racing.

He agreed to give it a try for a season so he sold the Cooper-Bristol and bought a Cooper-Alta, which he thought would be more competitive. Unfortunately, the engine kept breaking down and he bought a Bristol engine to install. This went much better and he soon came to the notice of the public because of his tail-out cornering style inherited from his days with the midget, which seldom travelled in a straight line. He naturally met the builder of his car, John Cooper, and the two became firm friends. Cooper invited Brabham to work at the Cooper factory in Surbiton, Surrey, although he was paid no wage. In return for his help in the factory, Cooper allowed him to build up a rear-engined Cooper-Bristol which proved to be very fast. It did not manage to win against the top-class opposition available in Britain, but he was able to mix it with the likes of Stirling Moss on wet tracks and he realised that, with a more competitive car, he could drive on equal terms with the Europeans. He took the Cooper-Bristol back to Australia, won the Australian GP with it and promptly sold the car before returning to England. With the proceeds of the sale he bought a 250F Maserati from the Owen Organisation for the 1956 Formula One season, but this car was very troublesome and almost bankrupted him before it got into a race.

John Cooper came to his rescue and asked him to drive for the works team, using the little bob-tailed Cooper Climax 1100 in sports car races and the new 1½-litre Coventry-Climax engined single-seater in Formula Two.

The year 1957 was the first season that Brabham (who had become known as 'Black Jack', because of his permanent five o'clock shadow) fully realised he could mix it with the Grand Prix stars and hold his own. The little four-cylinder Coventry-Climax engine was stretched to 2.2 litres in time for the Monaco Grand Prix and Brabham got the car into third place with three laps to go, only to have the fuel pump fail; so he pushed the car home to finish sixth. Brabham spent most of his time in Formula Two races where the little Cooper was very successful, but none of the other manufacturers had the wit to copy the Cooper, sticking instead to their ungainly front-engined cars.

Brabham took the 2.2-litre Cooper to New Zealand in early 1958 and won the New Zealand GP—his first win in five attempts. The rest of

*Above:* in the Spanish GP of 1970, Brabham took pole position, but retired from the front with a broken crankshaft. Here, he is leading Rodriguez, Ickx, Oliver and Pescarolo

*Right:* one of Brabham's unluckiest races was the 1970 Monaco Grand Prix when, with 19 laps to go, his BT33 was a comfortable 15 seconds ahead of Jochen Rindt in the Lotus 49C. However, Rindt whittled the lead down to 1½ seconds going into the last lap. The two were nose-to-tail as they entered the last corner when Jack locked his brakes and ran off the track only yards from the finish

the season wasn't so successful as there were several niggling faults with the Formula One car. The main problem was the gearbox, for Cooper was using an ordinary Citroën front-wheel-drive saloon car gearbox, but eventually it was completely stiffened and improved in other ways, and by 1959 Cooper had its own gearbox.

Still no one had cottoned on to the potential of the Cooper in 1959, and with all the problems sorted out and the engine now at a full 2½-litres Brabham began to win races; he started off with a victory in the Daily Express Trophy and followed up with wins in the British and Monaco GPs as well as several other good placings, which gave him the World Championship for 1959. He became the first British driver in a British car to

design the first Brabham car, which was originally called an MRD. The shy Brabham hated the thought of his name on a racing car, but he was eventually persuaded to name it a Brabham.

Brabham's first Formula One car appeared during 1962, using a Coventry-Climax V8 engine, and was first raced at the German Grand Prix where he retired. Later in the season he gained a second place at the Mexican Grand Prix. In 1963, he won the Australian, Solitude and Austrian Grands Prix and, in 1964, was third in the French Grand Prix at Rouen, a race which gave team mate Dan Gurney his first championship Grand Prix victory and the first ever championship victory for a Brabham car. Brabham, in fact, had to wait until 1966 for a Grand Prix championship win in his own car.

By this time, the 3-litre engine capacity limit had been imposed on Grand Prix racing and the Australian Repco company developed a V8, 3-litre engine for use in the Brabham. Although not the most powerful motor on the circuit, it was extremely reliable and that year the nimble Brabham machines earned their maker victories in the French, British, Dutch and German Grands Prix. Thus, Jack Brabham gained not only his third World Championship title, but the manufacturers' championship as well, a feat that no other man in motor racing has achieved. For this, he was awarded the OBE.

In 1967, Brabhams were again all-conquering, but this time it was Brabham's number 2, the burly New Zealander, Denny Hulme, who swept all before him.

In 1968, however, Jack's luck was out. The new 40hc Repco engine proved ·troublesome and, for 1967, Brabham turned to the Ford, Cosworth motor. He won the Silverstone International Trophy, but during the season had several retirements due to unreliability. However, he had a better end to the year, finishing fourth in the US Grand Prix, third in the Mexican Grand Prix and second in the Canadian Grand Prix.

He started the 1970 season well, winning the South African Grand Prix in his new monocoque BT33, and seemed certain to win the Monaco and British Grands Prix, but in both races last-lap troubles (an error at Monaco, running out of fuel at Brands Hatch) held him down to second place. He later finished third in the French Grand Prix and eventually finished in fourth place in the 1970 drivers championship. His last race was the 1970 Mexican Grand Prix, after which 44-year-old Brabham announced his retirement and returned to Australia, having sold the Brabham company to Bernie Ecclestone, who continued to race the cars using Brabham's name.

During Brabham's twenty-year career he took part in 127 World Championship races, of which he won 14, gaining three world titles. His successes in 1959 and 1960 pioneered the development of the rear-engined Grand Prix car which dominates racing today. His own cars, however, were evolutionary rather than revolutionary and Brabham's successes, therefore, are the result of careful planning, proven engineering techniques and painstaking preparation. The quiet Australian's dependability and professional approach to racing, together with his courage and dedication, have earned him a unique place in motor racing's hall-of-fame.                MT

win the championship.

Brabham's shyness and dislike of publicity was put to the test in the celebrations of his victory and it is certain that he did not capitalise on the win in the way that Stirling Moss would have done. In 1960, the Cooper was even more successful and Brabham won the Grands Prix of Belgium, Holland, France, Britain and Portugal to clinch the Championship comfortably.

For 1961, Formula One changed to 1½-litres and Cooper's dominance ended, but it had paved the way for the rear-engined revolution that was to come. In 1961, Brabham shook up the Indianapolis establishment with his ninth place in the Formula One Cooper, but he had few other victories that year, for the Coopers were thoroughly outclassed.

In 1961, Brabham decided to build his own cars, an ambition which he had long nurtured because he only felt safe in a car which he had personally constructed or supervised. He was allowed to do this at Cooper, but when called upon to drive other cars such as the Aston Martin sports cars and a Formula One Lotus he drove briefly in 1962, he was never fully competitive because he did not know every part of the car intimately.

By now, he was a successful garage owner in Chessington, with a tuning business as well, and his friend, Phil Kerr, came over from Australia to manage it, while Ron Tauranac joined him to

# EVOLUTIONARY RATHER THAN REVOLUTIONARY

Brabham cars have been the mounts of two World Champion racing drivers, one of them Jack Brabham himself—the only man to win the Championship in a car of his name

*Above:* during 1966/7, the Brabham team swept all before them with their 3-litre Brabham-Repco V8's. In 1966, Jack Brabham won the French, British, Dutch and German GPs, to become World Champion, while the following year, Brabham cars were victorious in the Monaco, French, German and Canadian GPs, gaining the World Championship for Denny Hulme

*Right:* the first Formula One Brabham was introduced at the 1962 German Grand Prix. The car's first championship victory was at the 1964 French GP, in the hands of Dan Gurney

*Opposite page, from top to bottom:* the BT44, Brabham's F1 contender for 1974; Jack Brabham and designer Ron Tauranac in conference; Brabham leads a gaggle of cars at the 1970 Dutch Grand Prix; Brabham participating at Clermont Ferrand during the 1970 French GP

JACK BRABHAM was already twice World Champion when he decided to enter the racing-car-manufacturing business in 1961. Brabham, a self taught engineer, and his fellow Australian, Ron Tauranac, a racing car designer, formed Motor Racing Developments Ltd. During the first ten years of operation, the company became one of Europe's largest racing-car manufacturers. The cars achieved long lists of victories and always reflected the sound and conservative engineering talent of Brabham and his partner. From their

humble beginnings, the Brabham cars went on to win two World Championships for their drivers and it was only when circumstances conspired to prevent Brabham and Tauranac continuing in their conservative ways that the fortunes of their cars began slowly to wane.

The first car was built for Formula Junior in 1961, but that was strictly an MRD. The following year saw the introduction of a true Brabham in Formula One, at the German Grand Prix. Powered by a Coventry-Climax V8 engine, driving through a Colotti gearbox, the car was essentially conventional by the standards of its time, though these standards (which incorporated such features as a space-frame chassis, engine behind the driver, all-independent suspension, etc) had been but recently established. In the details of its suspension, particularly at the rear, it most resembled the contemporary Lola. Tauranac refused to change the basic design and follow the new fashion for stressed-skin chassis construction; for the remaining years of the $1\frac{1}{2}$-litre formula, the Brabham was essentially the same. It was always one of the lightest cars in the field, and apparently well balanced, although its deficiency in torsional stiffness robbed it of slow-corner capability. Tauranac argued that a measure of torsional flexure was of value in really fast bends and evidence suggests that the car was faster than average through them. The fact that Jack Brabham was difficult to overtake on twisty circuits was really due to his driving technique, for his team mate, Dan Gurney (who wore out his front tyres as rapidly as Brabham wore out his rears), enjoyed no such immunity.

In 1965, a revised chassis was designed to accommodate the new flat-16 engine promised by Coventry-Climax. When that promise was withdrawn, the chassis was adapted for the Tasman series of races (for $2\frac{1}{2}$-litre cars) with a view to serving as a full 3-litre Formula One car in 1966. That year was the first of the 3-litre formula for Grands Prix, and it was to be expected that a number of the cars competing would be rather makeshift improvisations. Many of them were cars that had been exercised during the winter in Australasia, where a $2\frac{1}{2}$-litre Tasman formula survived; and in fact some Brabham chassis, fitted with four-cylinder Coventry-Climax FPF engines, were run in the European season for more than two years. One of them crashed during a practice session at Silverstone, killing its driver, the private entrant Bob Anderson.

Against this background of general unreadiness, the new 3-litre Repco Brabham appeared complete and ready—and extremely competitive—on the first day of the year, at East London, for the South African GP. Only the failure of a proprietary fuel-injection pump robbed it of victory on its first outing; clearly the car was very lively and a triumph of moderation in its design and construction. It was very many years since a car of such unworldly simplicity (by the standards of its day) could have been so immediately competitive.

The chassis was based on the 1965 $1\frac{1}{2}$-litre prototype, with a simple, multi-tubular space frame giving a mere 1000 lb ft per degree of torsional stiffness at a time when all other constructors were using stressed-skin hull construction and claiming figures twice or even five times as high. Because of its origins, the car had a narrower track than most rivals, but it had front suspension that was better arranged than most to deal with brake torque reaction, and its small wheels (another legacy of $1\frac{1}{2}$-litre practice) were shod with new tyres of distinctive appearance and uncommon adhesion, bearing witness to the new interest being taken in European racing that year by the American tyre manufacturers (Brabham was the first to use Goodyear tyres in GP racing, a year or two earlier). Aerodynamically, the only matters requiring comment were that the front spring and damper units were exposed in the airstream instead of being concealed within the body as in most rivals, and the exhaust pipes, further aft, also increased frontal area and drag.

The engine was even more disarmingly naïve. It was a very clever adaptation by the Repco engineer Phil Irving (of some fame in the motor-cycle industry), of the light-alloy cylinder block of an American passenger car, the Oldsmobile F85. On to this had been grafted special cylinder heads carrying parallel valves in line with each other, and operated by a single overhead camshaft—simply because of the constraints imposed by the existing chassis frame! The outcome was a modest, but adequate, power output (285 bhp at the beginning of 1966, later 300 bhp) with a generous spread of torque over a wide range of rpm.

Of Brabham's rivals, only one was to offer consistent stern opposition to the triumphant 1966 progress of the eponymous Jack Brabham. This was the modified 2-litre Lotus 33 driven by the late Jim Clark. It challenged very successfully on tortuous circuits such as Monaco and medium-speed ones such as Zandvoort, the Brabham surviving the ordeal by virtue of greater durability. On very fast circuits, the Brabham lacked sheer speed to compare with that of the 3-litre Ferrari. In a give-and-take season, the Brabham survived as the best all-rounder, the most durable finisher, the winner of the World Championship for Constructors and the mount of the World Champion driver. Against much sterner opposition it did the same the following year, when the team's second-string driver, Denny Hulme, won the championship. Never the fastest car on the track, nor the

most accelerative, and seldom the most agile, the Repco Brabham in those two outstanding years carried nothing to excess, but carried off nearly everything with success.

For 1969, the Brabham Formula One car was Ford-engined, as it has been ever since (and as virtually all Brabham F2 and F3 cars have been, with the remarkable exception of the 1966 F2 machines which were powered with devastating success by Honda), but so have been most of its more successful rivals. It seems, in retrospect, that the more the Brabham's design conformed with currently accepted dogma, the less successful it was, though there was a brief respite in the 1969 season, when the new team member Jacky Ickx carried off the German and Canadian GPs. The

soundness of this basic *ex post facto* judgment was supported in 1970 when the first F1 Brabhams, with stressed-skin chassis, had a lean year. They were not the first of the firm's cars to be thus built, for an unsuccessful Indianapolis contender was made in the same fashion a year earlier, while the current tubular-chassis F1 cars had been shorn of the diagonal tubes in their space frames, the necessary bracing being supplied by sheet metal panels. The change in 1970 was not a matter of choice, but was enforced by new safety regulations which insisted on bag tanks for fuel, in such terms that a multi-tube frame was impractical.

Having, in a sense, caught up with the rest of the Grand Prix chassis builders in technique, if not in results, there now seemed no reason why this technical

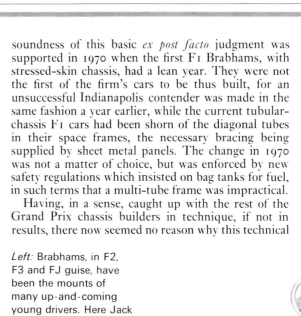

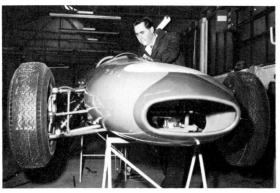

*Left:* Brabhams, in F2, F3 and FJ guise, have been the mounts of many up-and-coming young drivers. Here Jack Brabham supervises the assembly of one of the earliest cars to bear his name

*Above:* the 1963 Formula One Brabham was a conventional car by the standards of its time. It was powered by a Coventry-Climax V8 1.5-litre engine, mounted at the rear, and featured a space frame, independent suspension and a Colotti gearbox. The Brabham team was the first of the European Formula One manufacturers to use the American Goodyear racing tyres. This car was used until the introduction of the 3-litre engine capacity limit in 1966, although it was greatly modified

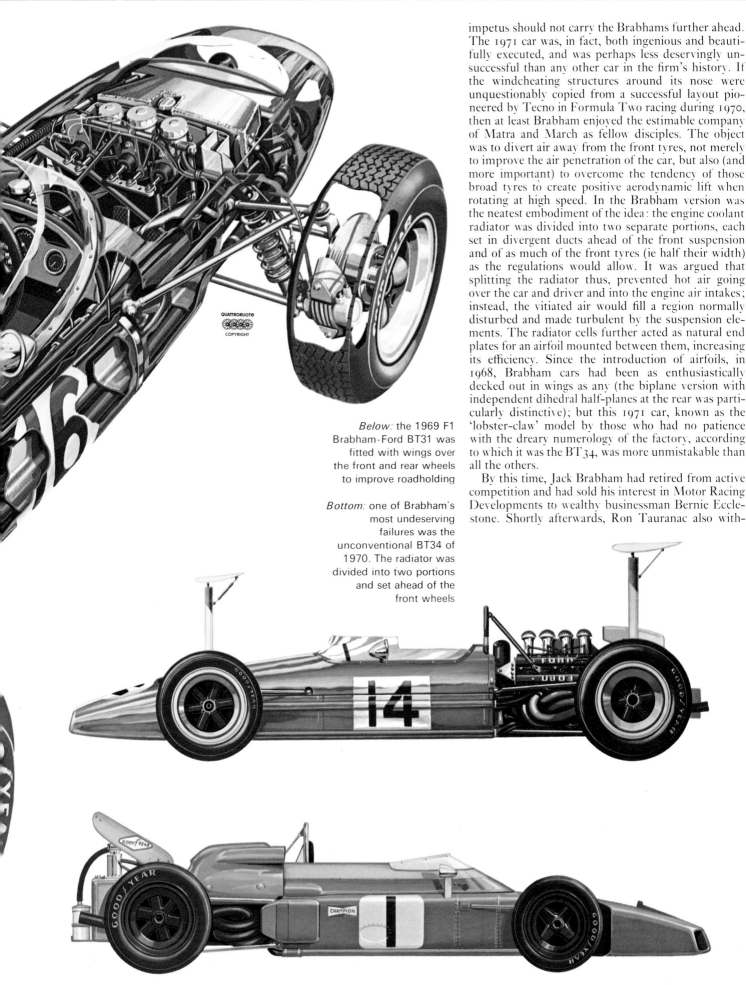

impetus should not carry the Brabhams further ahead. The 1971 car was, in fact, both ingenious and beautifully executed, and was perhaps less deservingly unsuccessful than any other car in the firm's history. If the windcheating structures around its nose were unquestionably copied from a successful layout pioneered by Tecno in Formula Two racing during 1970, then at least Brabham enjoyed the estimable company of Matra and March as fellow disciples. The object was to divert air away from the front tyres, not merely to improve the air penetration of the car, but also (and more important) to overcome the tendency of those broad tyres to create positive aerodynamic lift when rotating at high speed. In the Brabham version was the neatest embodiment of the idea: the engine coolant radiator was divided into two separate portions, each set in divergent ducts ahead of the front suspension and of as much of the front tyres (ie half their width) as the regulations would allow. It was argued that splitting the radiator thus, prevented hot air going over the car and driver and into the engine air intakes; instead, the vitiated air would fill a region normally disturbed and made turbulent by the suspension elements. The radiator cells further acted as natural end plates for an airfoil mounted between them, increasing its efficiency. Since the introduction of airfoils, in 1968, Brabham cars had been as enthusiastically decked out in wings as any (the biplane version with independent dihedral half-planes at the rear was particularly distinctive); but this 1971 car, known as the 'lobster-claw' model by those who had no patience with the dreary numerology of the factory, according to which it was the BT34, was more unmistakable than all the others.

By this time, Jack Brabham had retired from active competition and had sold his interest in Motor Racing Developments to wealthy businessman Bernie Ecclestone. Shortly afterwards, Ron Tauranac also with-

*Below:* the 1969 F1 Brabham-Ford BT31 was fitted with wings over the front and rear wheels to improve roadholding

*Bottom:* one of Brabham's most undeserving failures was the unconventional BT34 of 1970. The radiator was divided into two portions and set ahead of the front wheels

drew from the company. Ecclestone continued to enter the team in Formula One and although the Brabham BT34s and later the BT37s were not too successful, Carlos Reutemann did manage to win the 1972 Brazilian Grand Prix in a BT34.

For 1973, Brabham produced the BT42, designed by Gordon Murray, and the name Brabham was once again in the top half of the grids and the first three finishing places. The distinctive BT42, with its triangular section monocoque, went extremely well and secured several good places for its drivers, Carlos Reutemann and Wilson Fittipaldi.

For 1974, Brabhams ceased to produce 'customer' cars so they could concentrate wholly on Formula One, with the BT44.

The BT44 was a progressive development of the

BT42, with the same triangular-section chassis, but with a much sleeker body that rose from the cockpit area, over the engine, and blended in with the airbox. The car also had a very small frontal area designed to force air over the car rather than under it. The fuel tanks had also been repositioned to give the BT44 a lower centre of gravity.

Works drivers for 1974 were Carlos Reutemann and ex-Formula Three star Richard Robarts.

Today the name Brabham is famous throughout the world, for producing well designed and well constructed machines. Such is their influence that several of the world's top drivers owe part of their success to Brabham, having used the company's products either in Formula Two or Formula Three guise, to reach the top.

*Top:* the wedge-shaped Brabham BT41 was introduced in 1973 and used in Formula Three events

*Above:* The 1973 F1 Brabham BT42 was designed by Gordon Murray. Driven by the South Americans Carlos Reutemann and Wilson Fittipaldi, it scored several good places during the season

# THE THEORY AND PRACTICE OF BRAKING

As cars go faster and faster, ever-greater demands are made of their braking systems. Brakes of today are highly efficient and their use is a skill in itself

BRAKES ARE devices for retarding or stopping a vehicle, usually by checking the rotation of some or all wheels. Although there have been instances of this work being allotted to electromagnetic eddy couplings, air compressors or even retro-rockets, the friction brake has been the only wholly successful means since the beginnings of motoring. In this type of brake, the energy of motion must be translated completely into heat energy, so that the efficiency of the brake depends entirely on how quickly this translation takes place and how quickly the heat is dissipated.

Early adaptations of horse-drawn vehicle practice, with a friction block rubbing on the rim of a road wheel, were soon abandoned on early motor vehicles. Flexible bands, lined with a friction material such as leather, were wrapped around drums attached to the wheels (or to a live axle) and tightened by the action of the driver's brake lever or pedal. These external-contracting or 'band' brakes survived, notably in the USA, until the 1920s. Long before then, the internal-expanding drum brake was proved much more effective: in it, rigid metal segments or shoes faced with friction material were pressed against the interior cylindrical surface of the drum, from which dirt, moisture and other contaminants might be excluded more effectively.

*Above:* a set of linings, ready to be fitted to brake shoes. The asbestos used is the best friction material and the fibres are moulded or woven into a resin matrix

*Right:* the massive drum brake at the front of Ferrari's 1953 GP car. The edge of the drum was finned for extra cooling. It was not long before discs had ousted drums on Formula One cars (Jaguar had used them in the 1952 Mille Miglia)

It was soon recognised that the best friction material was asbestos; and so it remains to this day, the fibres being moulded or woven densely in a resin matrix, sometimes with inclusions of copper, zinc or aluminium to ensure high-temperature stability. Other design features, intended to help dissipate the heat built up during braking, included the use of high-conductivity alloys for the shoes and drums, as well as finning and ventilation of the latter. If the brake becomes too hot, the friction material is likely to lose its efficiency, and hydraulic brake fluid may boil.

Drum brakes remain in use today, and only in the details of their construction do they differ from the earliest examples. Such alterations have been made to improve power, stability of performance or behaviour at high temperatures—but to some extent, the requirements of these factors are mutually exclusive. Thus a large-diameter brake is more powerful than a smaller one, but more affected by thermal expansion which causes the drum and shoes to adopt different radii and thus to lose contact over most of the friction area. More power was therefore sought from a drum brake of a given size, and this was found by exploiting the self-operating tendency of a shoe pivoted about its trailing end. Originally, the usual two shoes were forced apart and into contact with the drum by a single wedge or cam: the relative motion of the drum was accordingly from leading end to pivot for one shoe, and opposite for the other. By placing the shoe pivots diametrically opposite each other and using two cams, both shoes can be given the same action; and the twin-leading-shoe brake, in which both shoes do equal shares of work and tend to fit themselves more firmly against the drum surface, when applied, has proved more powerful. It is also more fierce and more sensitive to heat, but only in cars employing strong servo assistance (a servo derives power from the engine to boost the effort of the driver's leg) could the more stable but less powerful alternative of two trailing shoes be used for all four wheels. To give adequate braking response when the car is travelling in reverse, the rear brakes usually remain of the one-leading/one-trailing variety. Because of weight transfer onto the front wheels during deceleration, the front brakes bear the brunt of the work when the car is braked from high speeds, and this compromise is fairly satisfactory, but a very few cars (notably in racing, where stability and freedom from grab are most important) have had parallel-action shoes which are moved strictly radially against the drum surface.

The degradation of braking performance at high temperatures remains an insoluble problem of the drum brake. The shoes and linings are difficult to cool, heat distorts the drums, differential thermal expansion impairs good contact between drum and linings, and the resulting local high pressures and temperatures can cause temporary loss of friction in the linings, producing a form of failure known as fade. In the 1950s, the disc brake was adopted: it was an adaptation of the type already developed in aviation, where the same problems had beset heavy bombers twenty years earlier.

The principle of the disc brake was not new, occasional examples being tried in motor cycles in the 1920s and in machine tools even earlier. It substituted a flat disc for the drum, and the faces of this disc were nipped between fairly small pads of friction material, carried by a suitably robust 'caliper'. In such a brake, there is no danger from expansion of the heated disc, which remains flat; the pads are flat and small, avoiding risks of distortion there. All surfaces subjected to frictional heat are exposed to the air, the greater part of the

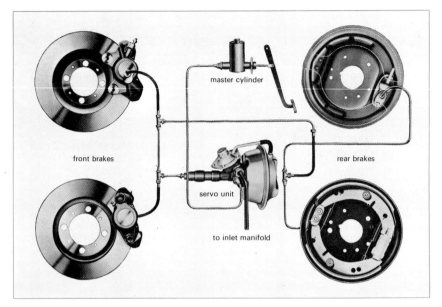

disc surface being free to shed its heat even during braking when only a small portion of it is being masked and heated by the pads. The disc may even be 'ventilated'. In this case it's two faces are separated by radial passages, open to the air at the outer edge, thus promoting an internal flow of cooling air.

A disc brake possesses no self-wrapping or unwrapping tendencies. In other words, it has no self-servo effect. Because of this and of the relatively small size of the friction pads, considerable force is needed to

*Above:* a typical hydraulic-brake layout. The servo is vacuum operated, the vacuum being created in the inlet manifold

*Left:* there are two basic types of drum brake: single-leading shoe (*above*), where one cylinder operates both shoes, and twin-leading shoe (*below*), where there is a separate hydraulic cylinder for each shoe, so that the movable end of each faces against drum rotation

*Top right:* the disc brake was widely adopted for car use in the '50s, although the idea had been tried, on motor cycles, in the '20s. This type of brake has many advantages over the drum, not least its ability to loose heat quickly

*Centre and bottom right:* exploded diagrams of typical master and wheel cylinders used in a hydraulic system

*Far right:* in recent years, racing and high-performance cars have become so fast that solid discs cannot dissipate heat quickly enough. The solution has been found in separating the two friction surfaces of the disc, thereby adding ventilation

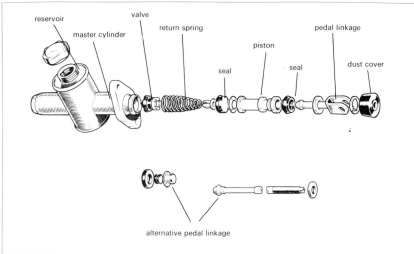

reservoir • valve • master cylinder • return spring • pedal linkage • piston • seal • seal • dust cover

alternative pedal linkage

piston • wheel cylinder • dust cover • seal • seal • piston • dust cover • locating plate • retaining circlip • bleed nipple

depressed, it moves the piston in the master cylinder and sends special fluid down a pipe to the 'slave cylinders' fitted to each brake. Their pistons move a corresponding amount (the liquid is incompressible) and movement is communicated to the shoes or pads.

This type of brake had been used earlier by some makers; some were even literally hydraulic, employing water as the fluid, as in the Grand Prix Duesenberg and Bugatti of 1921 and 1922 respectively. Nowadays, the fluids used are made just for that job, having a boiling point considerably higher than that of water. If the fluid boils, it forms vapour locks in the system and the compressible nature of these leads, at best, to a 'spongy' pedal and, at worst, to a complete loss of braking action.

The disc brake brought, in its turn, a widespread adoption of servo aids, usually energised by engine inlet manifold depression—although this form of so-called vacuum servo was displaced, as early as 1955, by an engine-pumped, high-pressure, 'powered hydraulic' system in the then new Citroën DS and, in a slightly simpler form, in racing Jaguars two years earlier.

Considerable development work has refined the disc brake in every detail since its introduction, but the principles have remained intact. More change has been apparent in the operating system, as always throughout the history of motoring. In the pioneer days, brakes were applied to the rear wheels only, through linkages worked by hand or foot. Four-wheel brakes appeared in 1909, to become general by 1930—by which time mechanical servo motors, driven off the gearbox, had become a popular feature of heavy luxury cars and most Grand Prix racers. By this time, too, it was a general practical or legal requirement that a car should have primary and secondary braking systems, the former applying all four brakes in response to the pedal, the latter applying two (usually checking the rear wheels) via a hand lever and being used for parking or to supplement a weak pedal system. This division of primary and secondary systems has been obscured by more recent legislative requirements for

squeeze them against the disc and an operating system of great efficiency and minimal lost motion or backlash is essential if slight wear of the pads is not to be translated into unacceptable travel of the driver's pedal. It was the widespread adoption of hydraulics for brake operation that made the use of disc brakes feasible in the 1950s, when it would have been beyond the capabilities of the mechanical systems generally favoured earlier. These hydraulic brakes have a 'master cylinder' connected to the brake pedal. When the pedal is

two separate circuits, designed to retain balanced and safely distributed braking action in response to the pedal, even if one circuit should, for some reason, fail.

Other recent developments include mechanical, hydraulic, pneumatic or electronic sensors to detect incipient wheel-lock during braking and inhibit it automatically, so as to reduce the risk of skidding on slippery surfaces; and the more general adoption of powered hydraulics is being energetically propounded by some manufacturers.

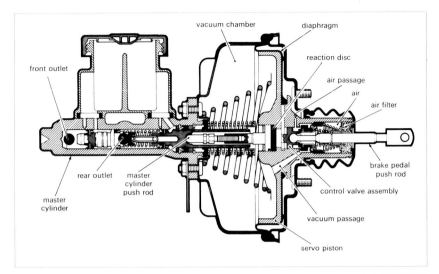

*Above:* a sectional drawing showing the important components of a Lockheed vacuum servo. The hydraulic systems in this unit are split so that either the front or rear brakes will continue to work should the other pair fail

*Right:* a pair of disc-brake pads; the linings are similar to those for shoes, but they are always bonded to the backing material. Changing disc pads is far simpler than changing shoes, as there is no brake drum to be removed the pads being slid into the caliper

# THE ART OF STOPPING

DECELERATION IS a state of affairs, but phenomena associated with the design of the vehicle or the state of the road may transform it into an event. The steady-state condition is rather rare and the occasions when a constant rate of deceleration is achieved by a constant pressure on the brake pedal occur very seldom on the road, though most drivers are unconscious of their instinctive modulations of braking effort and steering to correct losses of equilibrium.

For a start—for a stop?—do not kick the brake pedal hard, even for an emergency. Squeeze it gradually from the slightest pressure to as much as it will take without the wheels locking. This precaution need occupy only a fraction of a second, but if omitted the result will probably be a skid—straight ahead if the front wheels lock together, sideways if the rear wheels or only one wheel should lock. More sensitive treatment of the pedal allows all wheels to be held just short of locking point, which yields optimum braking: one of the many peculiarities of the tyre is that it gives maximum retardation when slipping by about 11%, so that at 50 mph the brakes should be holding the wheels back to a rate of rotation equivalent to 44 mph. Overstep this mark and the rate of retardation falls

dramatically and dangerously: what tyre technicians call the 'peak-to-locked ratio' varies from about 1.5 at 30 mph to as much as 8 at 80 mph, which means that the stopping distance is multiplied correspondingly when the car is sliding on locked wheels. Sensitive gradation of pedal pressure allows the driver to feel just how much braking the road surface will allow—and it is worth remembering that roads have many different characteristics, especially when wet: some offer only a twentieth as much grip as others.

If the wheels on one side of the car are on a wet surface and those on the other side are on a dry one, then strong braking will cause the tyres on the more slippery side to lock prematurely and the car will, if unchecked, go into a spin. Once again it is necessary to ease the brakes as the wheels begin to lock, and then apply them firmly again, repeating the sequence as often and as rapidly as required; and in this particular case some steering correction will be wanted as well.

Supposing that the road surface is good and the tyres and brakes are in perfect condition, what can be achieved? The classical laws of physics show that it is impossible to achieve a deceleration greater than the acceleration due to gravity, which is approximately 32 feet per second per second and equivalent to stopping in 30 feet from 30 mph. The classical laws of physics are fortunately wrong—or rather, inadequate, since they do not take such phenomena as tyre hysteresis (or energy absorption) into account. Current racing cars are capable of braking 1.7 times harder—we express this as 1.7$g$—and figures as high as 2.2$g$ have been recorded. Nevertheless 1$g$ is about the limit for most ordinary roadgoing cars in current production.

Fade is a condition that affects brakes when they are overheated by excessive use. It is a loss of braking power that may build up progressively or manifest itself quite suddenly—depending *inter alia* on the nature of the friction material used for brake linings or pads. Frequent heavy use of the brakes, as when driving hard down a twisting hill, is the most likely cause; but it can also be brought about by continuous gentle use of the brakes (as when checking the car's speed down a long, steep hill) because if they are worked without relief they have no opportunity to shed the heat that builds up in them.

Drum brakes are more sensitive than discs to heat, and give a more tangible warning of their loss of effectiveness by increased pedal travel. The feel of such a system has its antithesis in a powered-hydraulic disc system (such as that of the larger Citroëns) in which there is no pedal movement at all, the control responding purely to pressure. Brake response is something that has to be learnt empirically in each car: in one, the rate of retardation may increase progressively (that is, 50 lb force at the pedal will achieve deceleration twice as rapid as 25 lb force), but in another the increase may be disproportional. With practice, the driver's foot learns sensitivity to these things.

Another technique that needs practised acquisition before employment on the public highway is heel-and-toe braking. Here, the heel (or side) of the braking foot is applied to the accelerator at the appropriate time to accelerate the engine for a downward gear-change while braking is maintained. The object is not to supplement the brakes by engine braking, but to ensure that braking may continue uninterrupted by the necessity for effecting a downward change of gear for whatever reason. Engine braking can certainly be useful—it is a valuable adjunct to smooth driving—but it is not a particularly economical or efficient method of slowing down. With some forms of automatic

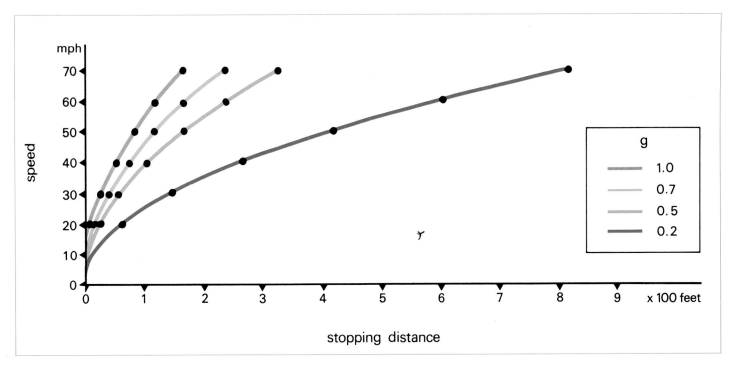

The graph above shows how stopping distances, at different speeds, vary with the retarding force. 'g' represents the acceleration due to gravity, which is approximately 32 feet per second per second. 1.0 g is the theoretical maximum which can be obtained, but in practice as much as 2.2 g has been recorded

transmission installed it may, in any case, be impossible.

Many of the finer points of braking technique are bound up with the behaviour of the car on its suspension (including the tyres) when the brakes are in use. The most obvious effect is that of forward weight transfer: because the centre of gravity of the car is above the level of the road (where the braking force is applied in the contact area between road and tyres), there is a tendency for the car to tip forwards when decelerating. The higher the centre of gravity, or the shorter the distance between it and the front wheels, the greater this nose-down pitch will be. Its effect is to increase the load on the front tyres and commensurately to decrease that on the rear tyres; and from this it may be deduced that the harder the braking, the more of it the front brakes and tyres have to do and the less those at the rear can do, until the limit is reached where the rear tyres are off the road and the front wheels are doing all the braking.

This is why front brakes are commonly larger and more powerful than back brakes. Some cars enjoy the refinement of a pressure-limiting device which reduces the braking effort applied to the rear brakes in proportion to the load carried by the rear tyres: this is mechanically operated by a linkage which measures the extension of the rear suspension. An inferior substitute for such a mechanism is the process known as 'cadence braking', in which the driver is recommended to increase his braking effort to the wheel-locking maximum as the nose of the car pitches downward, and then to release the brakes and allow it to recover its equilibrium before repeating the cycle. The process is self-defeating: if the pitch frequency is low, too much time will be lost in the non-braking portion of the cycle, and if the pitch frequency is high enough to overcome this objection it will be too rapid for the driver to match it effectively.

A more complex aspect of weight transfer is introduced by the tyres. The more heavily they are laden, the more braking effort they can transmit—but only up to a certain point, beyond which further increases of load effect no further improvement. A car designed to exploit forward weight transfer in braking may not be able to achieve it in slippery conditions, when the front tyres skid before a high enough braking force is

available to pitch more weight onto them: the rate of deceleration is then limited to what the front tyres can achieve in this lightly-laden state. This used to be a common failing of tail-heavy cars.

Weight transfer effected by braking will alter the cornering ability of all four tyres, and lateral weight transfer to the tyres on the outside of a corner will alter the braking ability. Depending on the generosity of the tyre size in relation to the load they carry, and also on the state of the road surface, a car's cornering ability may be increased or decreased by braking while cornering—and it will also depend on the severity of the braking. Skilled competition drivers may use the brakes to reduce or increase understeer right up to the apex of a corner, or indeed to produce any desired effect from a stright-forwards slide to a full spin. The latter is in fact a very effective way of stopping a car in the shortest possible distance, but it is emphatically not a technique for the road car, which may easily overturn in the attempt. The ordinary driver is better advised to stick to the time-honoured advice to get all his braking done while travelling in a straight line before the corner, and to leave the brakes alone while going round it. He would also do well to remember that when the front wheels have been locked by heavy braking, they can do no steering.

What if the brakes fail? At times like these, it pays to be one of the specially skilled fraternity. Changing down to as low a gear as can be reached and relying on engine braking is all very well if there is plenty of room to slow down, but there seldom is enough for such gentle deceleration and it might be necessary to take to the hedgerows or scrape the side of the car against a wall or (best of all) a snowdrift. Such facilities are not always available, alas, and that is when the skilled driver scores: using the handbrake hard enough to lock the rear wheels may not achieve much retardation (handbrakes seldom achieve better than 0.25$g$) but in conjunction with nicely timed steering he may be able to slew the car sideways or spin it, exploiting the lateral scrubbing of the tyres to slow the car while the gyration itself dissipates some kinetic energy. You see, advanced driving skills are worth acquiring; but the only safe place to do so is on the skid pan of an advanced driving school.　　LJKS

# THE BUSIEST MOTOR RACING CIRCUIT IN THE WORLD

In use almost every day of the week, either for racing or for testing, Brands Hatch is one of the most important and popular race tracks in the world

ALTHOUGH IT WAS NOT the scene of a World Championship race before 1964, Brands Hatch has a history of motor sport going back for longer than those of most circuits. Brands Hatch, which is on the main A20 Dover Road, twenty miles from London, was first used for racing in 1926, although the earliest races were for nothing more than bicycles. However, by 1928 motor cycles were using the course too, and by the time World War II began, Brands Hatch had become one of the leading grass track circuits in the south.

After the war, racing continued where it left off and, by 1947, its popularity was such that it was put on a commercial basis and the former association of motor cycle clubs, the Brands Hatch Combine, became Brands Hatch Stadium Limited, which was the forerunner to the present day company Brands Hatch Circuit Limited.

Racing became highly organised, on a kidney-shaped one-mile course in a natural amphitheatre, where most of this original part of the circuit can be seen from any point round the downland bowl. During this time and well into the 1950s the races were run in an anti-clockwise direction. In 1949, a decision was made to surface the track and the following year,

after an expenditure of £14,000, a road circuit was in existence, precisely over the top of the original grass track and still the original 1 mile in length. In April of 1950, cars (the little 500s of the Half-Litre Club, later to become the BRSCC) used Brands Hatch for the first time and, almost from that moment, cars started to gain prominence over motor cycles, although the latter are to be seen in action there to this day.

It was quite early in its career as a road circuit that Brands Hatch established its position as an all-year track, with the first ever Boxing Day car-race meeting in 1954, by which time the circuit had acquired an uphill loop called Druids Hill.

Within another year, the first announcements were made concerning the proposed extension of the course, which was by now $1\frac{1}{4}$ miles, to something close to the then-expected three mile lap suitable for Grand Prix racing. In fact, it wasn't until 1960 that this work was finally carried out and then the increase was to only 2.65 miles. The first race on the new, longer circuit was won by the then reigning world champion Jack Brabham driving a Cooper in the Silver City Trophy Race. This marked an important link with John Webb, who arranged the sponsorship with the Silver City

airline for whom he handled public relations.

A year later, the circuit was acquired by Grovewood Securities Limited, a property and industrial group taking its first steps into circuit ownership—to be followed, in subsequent years, by the purchase of the Mallory Park, Oulton Park and Snetterton circuits.

In 1961, Rothmans-Carreras, the tobacco group, took the plunge into race sponsorship with the Guards Trophy race (also won by Brabham), which was part of the championship series for the very short-lived Inter-Continental Formula cars (nearly all $2\frac{1}{2}$-litre cars from Formula One discontinued the previous season). It was, in fact, a good race and Rothmans continued their support for motor racing from then on. For 1962, however, the Guards Trophy race was held for sports cars. The same year (and again in 1963) there were six-hour saloon car races run by the British Racing and Sports Car Club, which became the 'resident' organiser for most of the main events, although the circuit's policy has always been to use a wide variety of organising bodies.

It was in 1964 that all the work to build up the circuit into a major racing venue reached its fruition. The Royal Automobile Club took the British Grand Prix to Brands Hatch for the first time, and a tensely close race was won by Jim Clark's Lotus-Climax less than three seconds ahead of Graham Hill's BRM after a

On a lap of Brands Hatch, we would first cross the start line on Top Straight (*above*). This is very bumpy and undulating, so it is important not to overbrake for Paddock Bend, lest the car bounce around. Paddock is a tricky, steep-downhill, reverse-camber bend, which, unless taken correctly, will throw the car to the left side of the circuit dangerously near to the grass. After Paddock, Pilgrim's Rise is a steep, uphill straight into the 180° hairpin, Druids (*above left*), that throws us into a sweeping, downhill left-hander, South Bank. Passing the rear of the pits, behind the start line, we enter South Bank bend, a tight, uphill left-hander that leads to the fast straight into the country. The straight falls into Pilgrim's Drop, the fastest part of the circuit, and then on to Hawthorn's Bend, a right-hand bend with a nasty bump in the middle of it that the car can easily bottom on. Portobello straight, at the far end of the circuit, leads into Westfield bend, a fairly orthodox right-hander, then into Dingle Dell, a right hand kink amidst a host of bumps and humps. Dingle Dell Corner is next, a totally blind right-hander that leads to Stirling's, a sharpish left-hand bend that puts us on the straight to the right hand bend, Clearways and out of the 'country'. Clearways is another Brands speciality, being a bend in two parts. We approach on the brow of a hill and steer down a short gradient with reverse camber, then take the long uphill section that sends us screaming past the grandstand and pits

race-long duel between these two drivers.

With its reputation confirmed as a World Championship track, Brands Hatch has henceforth had Formula One racing every season, irrespective of the whereabouts of the Grand Prix held on alternate years with Silverstone. From 1965, there was also a Race of Champions', Mike Spence (Lotus-Climax) putting his name in the record books as the first winner. At first, this event alternated with the Grand Prix, the next one being held in 1967. This was a year which brought another world championship event, the BOAC 500 (later to become the BOAC 1000, when the distance was increased from 500 miles to the sports car championship requirements of 1000 kilometres), with the Chaparral driven by Phil Hill and Spence winning; the Chaparral demonstrated the efficiency of aerofoils in motor racing for the first time before a British audience.

For the previous two years, long distance sports car races had been held, the 1965 event being a 1000 mile race (two 500 mile parts on consecutive days, won by the MGB of Warwick Banks and John Rhodes when more powerful machinery dropped out) and the 1966 race over 500 miles giving a win to the powerful 7-litre AC Cobra of Bob Bondurant and David Piper.

For 1968, a bumper programme was organised, with a Formula One Race of Champions as well as the Grand Prix, the BOAC 500 and all the rest of the meetings which, with testing, training and commercial demonstrations, made Brands Hatch the busiest motor racing circuit in the world.

A similar programme was staged in 1970 and for 1969 and 1971, years without a Grand Prix, there were the Race of Champions and BOAC events, plus about 80 other race metings and well over 200 other days of activity, which is the normal complement for this busy track.

In 1971, John Webb conceived the idea of turning the circuit's traditional October international meeting into a festival of celebration for the British World Champion (Jackie Stewart). The race ended in disaster, with Jo Siffert being killed in his BRM. Much criticism was levelled against the fire-fighting arrangements around the track, but from this horror was born a complete revision of circuit fire-fighting.

1972 witnessed one of the most ambitious race plans for many years, a super Formula Libre event with a £50,000 prize fund. The Rothmans 50,000, as it was known, was won by Emerson Fittipaldi who ran away with the race in a John Player Special from the moment the flag dropped after promises of Indianapolis and Can-Am cars failed to materialise. 1972 was a good year for Fittipaldi at Brands, he also won the Race of Champions and the British Grand Prix. However, the John Player Victory meeting to celebrate all this was won, albeit very luckily, by the Marlboro-BRM driven by Jean-Pierre Beltoise.

The year of 1973 was one of relatively low key for Brands Hatch, with the Grand Prix at Silverstone and, because of FIA inflexibility over the date (the one offered guaranteed a financial disaster due to the clashing with a large international event abroad), no BOAC 1000. However, history was made when the Race of Champions went to Peter Gethin in a Chevron Formula 5000 car, vanquishing the Formula One field in a mixed event.

Although relatively short by Grand Prix standards, Brands Hatch presents a major challenge, having some extremely difficult corners and a series of undulations in its 2.65 mile lap, while a surface of far from billiard table quality poses suspension problems of a high order.                                                    GM

---

Westfield Bend

Portobello Straight

Dingle Dell

Hawthorn Hill and Bend

Dingle Dell Corner

Stirling's Bend

Druids Hill Bend

Pilgrim's Drop

Pilgrim's Rise

Clearways

South Bank Bend

Paddock Hill Bend

Startline

# SPEND 5 MINUTES SAVE £45

EVERY YEAR, Britain's two major motoring organisations, the AA and the RAC, attend to three million vehicles which have broken down on the roads of the UK.

Add to that the commercial vehicles which suffer breakdowns, together with those private motorists who seek direct roadside help from garages, and the number of vehicles which come to grief every year on Britain's roads is probably about seven million.

A vehicle breakdown is expensive: not just in terms of the cash which has to be paid for emergency repairs or for a tow to a workshop, but in the time wasted waiting for assistance and in the general delay to a journey.

The minimum charge, by a garage, for a lift and tow of not more than three miles at night or on a Sunday is usually over six pounds. Running out of petrol on a motorway, involving a garage breakdown truck in a round trip of 30 miles, which is average, could cost a motorist up to seventeen pounds for the delivery of one gallon of fuel.

The AA recently analysed the cost to 188 motorists of their breakdowns on motorways in England. They paid out an average of £45 each for towing charges and repair costs, and a further nine pounds each for related costs such as hotel expenses, rail fares or hire car fees.

One in eight of the motorists questioned found that their vehicle came to a halt through loss of the fan belt—under more normal circumstances a replacement belt would cost about 55 pence.

According to Britain's motoring organisations the causes of most vehicle breakdowns follow a fairly predictable pattern which hardly changes from year to year.

Nearly one-third of the cars and lorries which grind to an unscheduled halt do so because of some failure of the vehicle's cooling system. This is usually because the fan belt has broken, but it can be caused by water hoses bursting or by radiator thermostats and water pumps failing.

About one-quarter of all breakdowns are caused either through deterioration of the battery or because some part of the ignition system has failed. Seven out of every 100 stranded cars, for example, are found to have worn distributor contact points.

Since the law was changed, making it an offence to use a vehicle fitted with defective tyres, the number of breakdowns caused by punctures has decreased. Nevertheless, seven drivers out of every 100 seeking emergency help from the motoring organisations do so because they have tyre troubles.

Sixteen per cent of all motorists who run into trouble have fuel problems, and only a minority of them suffer because of mechanical faults with a carburettor or a petrol pump. The main group in this category have simply neglected to get their fuel tank filled.

Out of the estimated seven million breakdowns which occur on Britain's roads every year, just over one-third are caused by serious mechanical failures such as engine seizures or major defects in gearbox and clutch units.

Every day 1300 cars break down on the UK's 1100 miles of motorway network and motorway police, who control the emergency telephone system, complain that many drivers do not know how to summon help.

All motorway telephones, whether painted RAC blue or AA yellow, are linked to police control centres. The police operator's job is to contact either the AA or the RAC if the caller is a member, or to summon a local breakdown garage.

The operator needs to know the location (the number and letters on the side of the telephone box), the

caller's name, and the make, model, colour and the registration number of the broken down car. Once this information has been passed it is important not to attempt to move the vehicle before assistance arrives.

Motoring organisations are similarly critical of the neglect and carelessness which results in so many drivers needlessly requiring help. They estimate that one-third of all breakdowns, both on motorways and on urban roads, could be eliminated if drivers would make a simple, five-minute check before starting any long journey.

Tyres, they say, should be inspected for wear or damage and should be inflated to the correct pressure whilst they are cold. The radiator should be topped up and the water hoses checked for leaks. The fan belt ought to be examined for wear and its tension checked. Evidence of deterioration in electrical leads to the engine or of dirt on connections should be corrected. The engine oil level should be inspected and the fuel tank topped up.

The few minutes spent making these checks would seem a small price to pay as an alternative to the frustration, expense and lost time resulting from a vehicle breakdown.                                    HL

*Above:* Britain's two main motoring organisations, the AA and the RAC, attend to over three million of the UK's seven million annual breakdowns. Both organisations are critical of the neglect and carelessness of the motoring public and estimate that one third of all breakdowns could be eliminated if drivers would make a simple five-minute check before starting any long journey

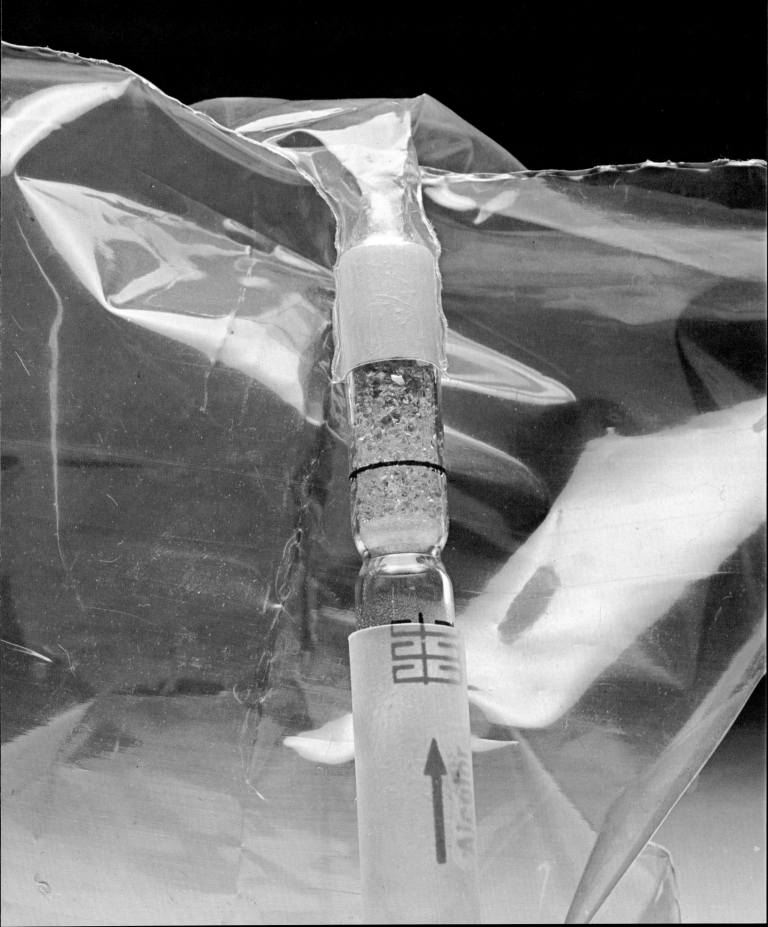

# LOOKING INTO THE CRYSTAL BAG

THE DAYS when the drinking driver could prove his sobriety by walking a straight line are over in the United States. Chemical tests have replaced the police officer's personal judgment of sobriety or drunkenness in every state of the union. As an indication of alcohol intake, the breathalyzer test can be very useful: it involves only one exhalation of breath, through alcohol-sensitive crystals into a plastic bag, and yet gives a fairly accurate assessment, which depends on the resultant crystal colour, of a driver's blood-alcohol level. The breathalyzer test is only one of several used throughout the USA. The actual type, be it saliva, blood, urine or breath, varies from state to state. If a chemical test shows that the percentage of alcohol in the driver's blood is above the statutory level, that's it. No amount of articulate argument or showy display of co-ordination will refute the presumption that he is operating a motor vehicle 'under the influence'.

In 1972, 56,000 people died on America's highways. Abuse of alcohol was a probable factor in 28,300 of these deaths. Faced with such macabre statistics, state and local governments began, in the late 1960s, to move toward the principle of applying scientific methods and standards to the drinking driver problem. Since the individual states of the US are responsible for all laws regulating traffic and driving, the federal government could only urge compliance of the state legislatures with model codes. One of the thirteen standards recommended for nationwide adoption by the National Highway Safety Bureau in 1967 dealt with alcohol in relation to highway safety. To be in compliance with the standard, each state was urged to establish specific test procedures for determining blood-alcohol content. The level of blood alcohol at which the bureau suggested that a driver be deemed intoxicated was 0.10 per cent by weight. The standard also urged state laws which would stipulate that a person placed under arrest for operation of a motor vehicle while intoxicated has given his implied consent to an alcohol test simply by the act of applying for and accepting a driver's license. While some states (Maryland, for example) still set the level of presumed intoxication as high as 0.15 per cent blood alcohol, the bureau's alcohol guideline has now been adopted in its broad outline throughout the country.

Despite claims to the contrary by practised drinkers, alcohol affects most people in similar and predictable ways. Inevitably, it reduces acuteness of perception and speed of reflexes. It also has the powerful psychological effect of impairing judgment and inhibitions. In the early stages of consumption, this factor may prove even more dangerous for the inexperienced or unstable driver than the factor of physical impairment.

Alcohol is absorbed directly into the blood stream through the blood vessels of the stomach and intestines and is subsequently distributed evenly in the water content of the body. Because of this, consumption of the same amount of alcohol will result in a lower concentration in the bloodstream of a 180 pound man than in that of a 130 pound man. Nonetheless, the alcohol begins to act on the brain swiftly. A person becomes intoxicated when he drinks more rapidly than his body can dispose of the alcohol intake by oxidation. Oxidation, however, is a slow process that cannot be speeded up by artificial means such as exercise, cups of coffee, hot or cold showers or the like. Thus, given the variables in the size of the drinker, the nature of the drink and the speed of consumption, an almost infinite number of drinking scenarios are possible. Three strong Martinis in an hour will usually bring a 220-pound man to a 0.10 alcohol concentration

level, while his 100-pound sidekick can reach the same level with three bottles of beer. If the 220-pounder had consumed beer instead of Martinis, he could have drunk the three bottles without exceeding the 0.05 level. The three Martinis would have boosted the 100-pound friend to an alcohol concentration of 0.22 and probably have placed him safely under the table. Regardless of how he gets to the 0.10 per cent level, that is where the drinker is judged by legal and medical authorities to have lost his capacity for safe driving.

There is no legal way to escape the chemical test. All states forbid driving under the influence of alcohol, and although their definitions of 'under the influence' still vary, they generally set a limit for blood-alcohol concentration of 0.10 or 0.15 per cent. If an amount of alcohol below the presumptive level (say 0.05 per cent) is detected in the driver's blood, this fact will simply be weighed with other evidence, but will not be regarded as conclusive. All states also now have laws that provide for testing of the breath, blood, urine or saliva of a driver charged with driving under the influence of alcohol. All these chemical tests are deemed equally valid and reliable for determining the concentration of alcohol in the blood. Most of them are administered by police officers, although Massachusetts law provides that the blood test can be administered only by a physician. Almost every state also has adopted the 'implied consent' provision alluded to above, which specifies that anyone holding a motor-vehicle operator's license automatically gives his consent to a possible chemical test if he is ever requested to submit to one by an arresting officer. No motorist in any state will be physically forced to take a test, but refusal will mean automatic revocation of his license (as in most cases will a conviction for drunken driving based on the test).

In the early days of chemical testing, motorists challenged the laws on the grounds that such tests violated their constitutional right against self-incrimination. But in 1966, responding to strong arguments of public policy, the US Supreme Court rejected this argument and stated that test results should be viewed as physical evidence analogous to fingerprints taken after a lawful arrest. No conviction for drunken driving based on the evidence of chemical tests has ever been reversed in the United States.

A final question concerns the likelihood of a driver being asked to submit to the chemical test. Almost without exception, police in the United States do *not* conduct random checks of motorists in search of potentially dangerous drivers. They do, however, keep their eyes peeled for any out-of-the-ordinary driving patterns, many of which constitute traffic violations in themselves. A driver stopped for any violation or erratic behaviour may, at the officer's discretion, be charged and requested to submit to an alcohol test.

The most common penalty on conviction is suspension or revocation of the driver's license, a practise that has not proved entirely satisfactory from the public-safety point of view. A recent California study showed that almost half the drivers whose licenses had been revoked continued to drive regardless. Some states (such as Iowa) are experimenting with laws that enable the court to commit a driver convicted of more than one drunken-driving charge to a state hospital for the rehabilitation of alcoholics. The question of how to deal with the dangerous drinking driver, once he has been identified, is a difficult one, yet to be resolved. Perhaps the best advice comes from the well known writer, Anon: 'If your cup runneth over, let someone else runneth the car'.                    JAP

CRAIG BREEDLOVE is one of a select band of Californian dragster fanatics whose sole hobby is attempting to go faster than the next man. He decided to build a car to crack the land-speed record but, lacking the enormous funds available to Donald Campbell, he designed a very simple car. He chose a General Electric J47 jet engine which was encased in a simple steel-tube chassis and fitted with a tricycle undercarriage. The aerodynamic shape and high tail fin gave the impression of an aircraft shorn of its wings and, indeed, that was virtually what it was.

Breedlove seemed unworried that his car did not comply with the FIA regulations; not only did it lack driven wheels, but only had three of them, when the regulations called for four wheels. However, the United States Automobile Club were prepared to recognise the attempt, as were the Federation Internationale Motocycliste, who regarded the vehicle as a three-wheeled motorcycle!

Breedlove ran out of money before the car was finished, but he was fortunate to obtain sponsorship and technical assistance from Shell and Goodyear. The car, patriotically named Spirit of America, began its first tests early in 1962 and it quickly worked its way up to 365 mph. The only major problem was its stability, but this was cured by modifying the fixed single front wheel so that it could be steered a few degrees from the straight ahead position. Prior to this, 'steering' had been effected by moving a small fin under the nose and by braking one of the rear wheels.

On 5 August 1963, the record attempt began. The course at Bonneville had been lengthened by two miles so giving Breedlove four and a half miles in which to get to maximum speed before going through the timed mile, after which there was a further four and a half miles for slowing down. Like most of the current record breakers, Spirit of America relied on a parachute for its main braking, the disc brakes only being used for braking to a standstill from 100 mph.

On his first run, Breedlove gave the car only 90 per cent of its available thrust and the average speed over the mile worked out at 388.47 mph. He knew that on the return run he would have to exceed 400 mph by a fair margin to beat Cobb's record. For this return run he gave the engine 95 per cent thrust and he sped over the flying kilometre at 428.37 mph, for an average speed of 407.45 mph.

Campbell, who was still pressing on with Bluebird, knew that he had little chance of exceeding Breedlove's record, for his car had all the complication of driven wheels, with gearboxes, drive shafts and, worst of all, tyres which were driven by the engine, which caused them to wear rapidly. Breedlove's tyres did not even need changing between runs. In July 1964, Campbell finally achieved two identical runs of 403.10 mph to break Cobb's seventeen-year-old record. It was, however, too late.

The Americans had decided to ignore the FIA's rules and the race was soon on to be first to 500 mph by any means possible, short of leaving the ground altogether. Breedlove was preparing for an attempt to beat his own record, but before he was ready Tom Green, in Walt Arfon's Wingfoot Express, raised the record to 413.2 mph. Three days later Arfons' brother, Art, raised it to 434.02 mph in his 17,500

horsepower Green Monster jet-powered four-wheeler, which had cost him little more than £5000 to build.

Breedlove made his attempt only a few days after the Arfons record, the Spirit of America now being fitted with a new and slightly more powerful engine. With almost insolent ease, he pushed the record up to 468.72 mph. Not content with that he went out again a few days later and became the first man to take the record over 500 mph, with an average of 526.28 mph. However, the return run almost ended in disaster, for his braking parachute snapped and the car careered unchecked for five miles before plunging through a row of telegraph poles into a lake. Breedlove managed to free himself from the car and swim to the shore.

Breedlove did not hold the record long, for Art Arfons came back with his crude Green Monster only twelve days later and, with the afterburner in full use, did two runs of 515.98 mph and 559.18 mph for an average of 536.71 mph.

Belatedly, the FIA decided to recognise records taken by cars with no driven wheels, but they refused to recognise records by three-wheeled cars. So the Green Monster's record was recognised, but not Breedlove's previous efforts. In an effort to get the official record back,

Craig Breedlove allowed his wife to drive Sonic I in 1965, and she now holds the land-speed record for women

Breedlove designed a new four-wheeled car around a 15,000 horsepower J79 turbojet engine. Called the Sonic 1, because of its believed ability to go through the sound barrier, the car was nothing more than a jet engine on four wheels, with a large rear stabilising fin. The car gave a great deal of trouble during testing and on one occasion went off course at over 600 mph, but it was gradually modified until it became stable at speed.

On 2 November 1965, Breedlove finally put his name in the FIA's record book, with a two-way run of 555.483 mph, still with plenty in reserve. However, the brave Art Arfons brought out his old Green Monster once again five days later promptly raised the record to 576.553 mph.

With the 1965 'season' almost finished, Breedlove decided to try and get back the record, and on 15 November he made his first run in Sonic 1 at 593.178 mph, following up with a fantastic return run of 608.201 mph to put in an average of 600.601 mph.

Breedlove's record remained intact until 1970 when Gary Gabelich raised it to 630.388 mph in his rocket-powered Blue Flame, but Breedlove was already planning a similar rocket-powered supersonic car complete with ejector seat!

In the meantime Breedlove had retained his interest in record breaking by planning to retake the wheel-driven-car record, using his early rival's car—none other than Donald Campbell's Bluebird. This project too was shelved.

Another record which fell to the Breedlove family occurred during the 1965 runs, when Craig allowed his wife Lee to drive Sonic 1. She made four runs with an average speed of 308.56 mph, so that the Breedloves are at present the fastest man and wife team on earth. MT

# A QUIET TOUCH OF CLASS

*Above:* the first of a famous line, the Bristol 400, was introduced at the Geneva Show in 1947. The engine was a 1971 cc, in-line 6-cylinder. The efficiency of the engine and the expensively made transmission, combined to give the 400 very high performance by the standards of its time. It had a live rear axle, sprung by torsion bars, and also featured independent front suspension comprising transverse leaf springs and forged upper wishbones

*Right:* the short-chassis, Zagato-bodied, Bristol 406S, of which only two were made. Almost perfect roadholding and an elegant lightweight body, made the car a delight to drive

THE BRISTOL is a British car which takes its name from the Bristol Aeroplane Company, which formed a car division in 1945. A small factory was established at Filton Aerodrome (near Bristol), where the company had its headquarters and where the cars are still made.

It was intended from the beginning that the cars should be built in small numbers and to the very highest standards in order to exploit the skills of the designers, inspectors and craftsmen who were recruited from the airframe and engines divisions of the company. Due to the presence on the board, during World War II, of a director of Frazer-Nash, which, before the war, had been an agent for BMW cars in Britain, an early decision was taken to base the design of the Bristol upon the immediate pre-war products of BMW, from whom drawings and know-how (particu-

larly that of their distinguished engineer, Dr Fiedler) were available. There was, at the time, some criticism of this choice, though it failed to take into account that the new Bristol embodied the best features of the BMW 326 chassis, 327 body and 328 engine. The entire design was subjected to minute scrutiny and considerable revision, the metallurgical improvement being especially noteworthy. Furthermore, the Bristol designers, since they were starting from scratch, undertook a detailed study of the scientific aspects of roadholding and handling, acquiring within a couple of years greater understanding and mastery of these than many other design teams in the industry. The result was that for a decade the controllability of the Bristol, its ride, handling, and cornering power, were of a standard only matched by outright purpose-built

competition cars and certainly not rivalled by anything of comparable luxury.

The first Bristol, the type 400, ran in prototype form in 1946 and made its debut at the Geneva Show in 1947. It was very much a hand-built car with virtually everything, except tyres, wheels, carburettors and electrics (to special specification), being made in the factory rather than bought from outside. Many of its design features set the pattern for subsequent models. The chassis was built from very deep box section fabrications and lay almost entirely within the wheelbase. The live rear axle, sprung by torsion bars, was

cross-over pushrods. This layout permitted the inlet ports to plunge vertically into the cylinder head, three downdraught carburettors giving free breathing characteristics. The efficiency of the engine and the expensively made transmission combined to give the type 400 a very high performance by the standards of its time, unhampered by the lightweight close-coupled 4-seater coupé body. Numerous competition successes were earned both in rallying and racing, but the car's main appeal was as a long-distance express of quality and virtuosity.

In 1949, the 400 was joined by a new design, the 401.

*Above left:* gathering of the clan. Pictured at a Bristol Owners' Club meeting are (from left to right) a 400, a 401, a 405 and a 405 drophead

*Above right:* close up of the beautiful Bristol 405 engine

*Below:* the author at Silverstone in his 405, which has non-standard wheels

linked to them and to the chassis at three points in such a way as to confine its movements to the vertical, eliminating the torque and roll effects from the steering.   The independent front suspension comprised a transverse leaf spring (so mounted as to be fully live) and forged upper wishbones, with the suspension and steering geometry refined to complement the studied characteristics of the tyres. The engine was an in-line 6-cylinder, of 1971 cc displacement, employing the best aero-engine materials and crowned by a cylinder head which gave it exceptional efficiency. Each combustion chamber was a polished hemisphere in which large valves were opposed; the single camshaft, in the crankcase, was connected to the inlet valves by pushrods, and to the exhausts (on the other side of the engine) by a secondary set of

Mechanically similar, it was distinguished by a body of more exemplary aerodynamic refinement. The stylistic inspiration came from Touring of Milan, but the actual contours were developed in Bristol's own wind tunnel to create a shape of very low drag. With the same 85 bhp engine and the same gearing as before, this car had better high-speed acceleration up to a maximum of 100 mph; with a higher axle ratio, the car proved capable of over 107 mph and covered 104 miles in one hour on the Montlhéry track. The body was of aluminium panelling over a steel tubular framework and, despite its 5-seat capacity and large luggage boot, it weighed only 1.2 tons. The Bristol 402 was a drophead version, of which only 24 were made. The 403 was an evolved form of the 401, announced in June 1953; it was externally unchanged, but extensive revisions to brakes, dampers, gearbox, heating and ventilation were accompanied by improvements to the engine, which acquired larger valves, a more sporting camshaft and a more robust bottom end, to make it capable of 100 bhp at 5250 rpm—still on the low-grade petrol of the time.

This engine was a detuned version of the racing unit that Bristol had been producing for some time to serve the requirements of other car manufacturers. The post-war history of Frazer-Nash, for example, was wholly based on it, and the emancipation of Cooper totally dependent on it. By 1952, the Bristol engine of Mike Hawthorn's Cooper developed 150 bhp, sufficient to catapult him to stardom. In subsequent years this race-proved engine was sought by other manufacturers, including AC, Lister, Lotus, Tojeiro and ERA. The G-type ERA, a Formula Two racer, was taken over by Bristol and adapted to make the basis of the Bristol 450, when the company decided to embark on its own racing programme. Its stiff tubular

chassis with de Dion rear axle and detachable-rim wheels bore little relationship to Bristol's production cars, but the engine and gearbox were essentially similar. The Bristol body, a closed two-seater, featured twin dorsal tail fins to ensure directional stability but, in its original form for the Le Mans race of 1953, was far from clean aero-dynamically. Experimental crankshafts failed before the race was over, but not before the Bristol had lapped five seconds faster than any other car of up to two litres capacity. Reversion to a standard crankshaft made it perfectly reliable and, at Reims and Le Mans, the Bristol team of three

car's polar moment of inertia in yaw and in pitch, was continued in all subsequent models.

The 405 continued in production from late 1954 as a saloon (297 examples) and a drophead coupé (43) until 1958. By this time the British Government had enforced some rationalisation of the aircraft industry, as a result of which it became necessary for the car division to be hived off as a separate limited company. Two very interesting prototypes—one an all-independently-sprung tourer with a 3½-litre, twin-overhead-camshaft engine, the other an ultra-low super-sports car with space-frame chassis—had to be

cars won class and team awards. The firm withdrew from racing at the end of the 1955 season, by which time the type 450 body had been redesigned twice—first as a very clean twin-finned coupé and then as a single-finned open car. The engine also underwent some development, the outstanding feature being a new twelve-port cylinder head giving even better volumetric efficiency.

While the 450 was still fairly new, Bristol put on the market a short-chassis luxury coupé, the type 404, which was soon christened the 'businessman's express'. Its styling was completely new and original: the unadorned radiator intake was based on that of the Bristol/Brabazon air liner; the two vestigial tail fins echoed those of the 450. There was a choice of engines: the touring two-litre gave 105 bhp, the sporting version, with a high-performance camshaft, gave 125.

Only 40 of these cars were made: not only was manufacture and inspection to aircraft standards, but the costing was done in the same way, with the result that this little car sold at a higher price than the full saloon—and newly punitive taxation, imposed shortly after its introduction, effectively killed it.

Much more successful was the 405, which reverted to the traditional 114-inch wheelbase, and carried a 4-seater saloon body with interior and exterior styling similar to that of the 404. The aluminium body had four doors (it was the only Bristol ever to do so) and, despite the use of some wood in the framework, it still weighed 1.2 tons. Mechanical revisions included the addition of an overdrive on the tail of the close-ratio four-speed gearbox. Among the noteworthy features inherited from the 404 was the provision of compartments in the front wings—one carrying the spare wheel, the other the battery and most of the electrical gear; and this feature which, by concentrating the weight near the centre of the car, reduced the

abandoned, and the new company's first production model revealed a change in emphasis. The 406 was less idiosyncratic in appearance, much more substantial and luxurious than the already fully-equipped 405. More torque and greater flexibility were obtained by enlarging the engine to 2216 cc. The same peak power of 105 bhp was reached at only 4700 rpm. The 406 was under-rated, but it was admirably detailed. It was among the first production cars to have four disc brakes, and the first of all to have its rear axle located laterally by a Watt linkage. This perfected the handling so much that a batch of six chassis with tuned engines were sent to Milan to be clad in lightweight four-seater grand touring bodies by Zagato. Two experimental

*Top:* Anthony Crook, who, with Sir George White, reformed the company in the '60s

*Above centre:* the 406 Bristol Zagato, only 6 of which were made. Alongside stand two of the standard 406 models

*Bottom:* the Bristol 406 used an in-line, 6-cylinder, of 2216 cc.

short-chassis cars were also built.

The most emphatic change came in 1961. It was clear that a much larger engine was necessary to satisfy the new demands of the market. Bristol's own new engine having to be abandoned for this reason, arrangements were made with Chrysler of Canada for a special version of their 5.2-litre V8 engine to be used in conjunction with Chrysler automatic transmission. This engine was rebuilt by Bristol with a high-lift camshaft and mechanical tappets, as well as a number of other detail modifications, and gave the Bristol 407 outstanding performance in its class. The car looked almost identical to the 406 but weighed

and many customers chose to keep their six-cylinder cars and rejoice in the sensual pleasure of their steering and gearchange, although the older models could not match the effortless superiority of the V8 performance. The 410, which came along in 1966, marked the point where Bristol once again could satisfy the demands of sporting customers while sacrificing nothing the sybarite might seek. All the major components were the same as in the 409 mark 2, as was the 132 mph maximum speed, but the acceleration was better, 100 mph being reached in 23 seconds from a standing start. More obviously its roadholding was improved, for the old sixteen-inch road wheels had

*Top:* the elegant interior of the Bristol 409

*Left:* The Bristol 409, which used a 5.2-litre Chrysler V8 engine. It was a revised version of the 407 and 408 and had improved suspension, higher gearing and power steering

*Above centre:* a driver's eye view of the Bristol 409 (*left*) and the unique spare wheel compartment built into the body panel of all Bristols from the 404 onwards (*right*)

*Bottom:* four Bristols all in a row (from left to right) 406, 408, 409 and 406

given way to fifteen-inch ones, for which a wider choice of tyres was available. Persistent development work on suspension added up to a considerable improvement in handling.

By this time the company had been reformed: no longer a limited company, it was simply a private partnership between Sir George White, Bt (grandson of the aircraft company's founder) and Mr Anthony Crook, an erstwhile racing driver who had been associated with Bristol since the days of the 400. Cars were still designed and made at Filton Aerodrome and a firm policy was established, according to which production would be strictly limited to a maximum of three cars a week; no concessions were to be made as to the quality of the engineering.

The expression of this policy appeared in 1969 as the Bristol 411. Still dimensionally and fundamentally like all its predecessors, but more restrained than ever in appearance, more exquisite than ever in its steering, it was more extreme than ever in its contrast of very quiet luxury with a performance that embraced a maximum speed of 140 mph with acceleration from 0 to 100 mph in under seventeen seconds. The engine of the 411 was a larger Chrysler V8 of 6.2 litres, still subjected to stripping, modification and re-assembly at Filton, to give a performance materially higher than the standard Chrysler engine.

Near the end of 1970 the 411 acquired self-levelling rear suspension, with two hydraulic jacks to adjust the settings of the rear torsion bars. Wider wheels with six-inch rims carried 205VR15 tyres. In May 1972 the bodywork was altered, a new front carrying four seven-inch headlamps, and this was the 411 mark 3. The Mark 4 appeared in the autumn of 1973, distinguishable externally only by different tail lamps, but internally by a larger Chrysler V8 of 6.5 litres running at a lower compression ratio to give the same performance as before on lower-grade petrol. The policy laid down some years ago is being adhered to strictly, and with every sign of success: at a 1973 retail price of £9,000 there was still a year's waiting list for this most exclusive of cars. LJKS

1.6 tons, and the front suspension was now by double wishbones and helical springs. Steering was no longer by rack and pinion and no longer gave the same eager and accurate responses, but the roadholding and balance were still good, and the car could exceed 122 mph with great ease in almost complete silence.

Two years later it was succeeded by the 408, mechanically almost identical, but with the body extensively restyled, particularly at the front where it now carried four headlamps. Late versions had the improved suspension, higher gearing and lighter transmission of the 409 which, in its turn, appeared in a revised form with particularly good steering.

The virtues of the 407, 408 and 409 were debatable,

## 411 series IV

Claimed by some to be the fastest true 4-seater touring car made, the series IV Bristol 411 represents all that is 'grand' in British grand touring cars.

Introduced at the 1973 London Motor Show, the 411 is powered by a 6½-litre Chrysler engine (modified by Bristol), producing a gargantuan 418 lb ft of torque which is enough to give it a top speed in excess of 140 mph and to push it to 70 mph in a mere 9.5 seconds. Not only has the car got tremendous performance, but with an 8.2:1 compression ratio, the car runs on 3-star petrol to the order of approximately sixteen miles per gallon.

Power is transmitted from the front-mounted engine, via a Torqueflite three-speed automatic transmission (standard) and a hypoid-bevel final drive to the rear wheels.

Front suspension is independent by wishbones, coil springs, an anti-roll bar and adjustable telescopic dampers. Rear suspension is by a live axle, longitudinal torsion bars, trailing lower radius arms, upper torque arms, transverse Watt linkage and adjustable telescopic dampers. An automatic levelling control is also used on the rear suspension to keep the car stable.

Braking is admirably taken care of by servo-assisted discs all round, giving a total swept area of 420 sq ins.

Power-assisted, recirculating-ball type, steering, along with the automatic transmission and the servo brakes, makes this 33 cwt car a lightweight to drive.

The elegant two-door four-seater body houses a sumptuous interior, which features leather reclining front seats, air conditioning (optional extra), electrically operated windows and an automatic speed control.

ENGINE: front-mounted 90° V8, water cooled. 110 mm (4.32 in) bore × 85 mm (3.75 in) = 6556 cc (400 cu in). Maximum power (SAE) 330 bhp at 5200 rpm; maximum torque (SAE) 418 lb ft at 3400 rpm; maximum engine rpm 5500. Cast iron cylinder block and head; compression ratio 8.2:1. 2 valves per cylinder operated by a single camshaft at the centre of the V. 1 Carter 4-barrel carburettor with automatic choke.

TRANSMISSION: Chrysler Torqueflite automatic transmission, hydraulic torque converter and planetary gears with 3 ratios. Maximum ratio of converter at stall 2; ratios 1st 2.45, 2nd 1.45, 3rd 1, reverse 2.2; hypoid-bevel final drive (ratio 3.07) driving rear wheels.

CHASSIS: Box-type ladder frame. SUSPENSION: front—independent by wishbones, coil springs, anti-roll bar and adjustable telescopic dampers; rear—live axle, longitudinal torsion bars, trailing lower radius arms, upper torque arms, transverse Watt linkage automatic levelling control and adjustable telescopic dampers.

STEERING: Recirculating ball, servo; 3 turns from lock to lock.

BRAKES: Servo-assisted discs all round; total swept area 420 sq in.

WHEELS: 6 in steel.

TYRES: 205 VR —15.

ELECTRICAL EQUIPMENT: 12 Volt, 71 Ah battery; 720-Watt alternator; Chrysler distributor; 4 headlamps.

DIMENSIONS AND WEIGHT: Wheelbase 114 in; track 54.5 in front, 55.25 in rear; length 194 in; width 68 in; height 57.50 in; ground clearance 5 in; kerb weight 3775 lb; turning circle 40 ft; fuel tank capacity 18 gals. BODY: saloon; 2 doors 4 seats (reclining front); electrically heated rear window.

PERFORMANCE: Speeds in gears —1st 50 mph, 2nd 90 mph, 3rd 140 mph plus; acceleration— 0—70 mph 9.5 secs, 0—100 mph 19 secs; gearing—26 mpg/1000 rpm; fuel consumption—approx 16 mpg.

# THE MOST IMPORTANT MOTOR RACE IN BRITAIN

*Left:* Jim Clark, rounding Druids Hill bend, at Brands Hatch, on his way to winning his third successive British Grand Prix in 1964

*Below:* the day Stirling Moss made history. In winning the 1955 GP at Aintree with a Mercedes'-Benz W196, Stirling became the first British driver to win the British Grand Prix

THE RAC BRITISH GRAND PRIX is already at least a quarter of a century old. 'At least', because the origins of the race are the subject of dissent. To call the 1974 race the 27th in the series is, for the organisers, the Royal Automobile Club, continuing a minor deception, for the 1948 race, first of the present series, was called the RAC Grand Prix and not the British Grand Prix, a title used the following year.

However, it is worth recalling that there were two British Grands Prix at Brooklands in 1926 and 1927, each won by 1½-litre Delage cars (the first by Robert Senechal and Louis Wagner, the second by Robert Benoist). Races called 'Grands Prix' were held at Donington Park from 1935 to 1938 inclusive and the last two were definitely worthy of the title, being contested by the Mercedes Benz and Auto-Union teams.

Since that time, the Royal Automobile Club has reserved for itself the name 'Grand Prix', although since 1971 it has been prepared to sell the name of the race to its sponsors (the Woolmark British Grand Prix in 1971 and the John Player Grand Prix—without the 'British'—since).

Ignoring the pre-war events, the British Grand Prix, as we know it today, has been held with the utmost consistency. Nearly all other races of at least equal antiquity have had gaps. Even the French Grand Prix was abandoned in 1955 after the Le Mans disaster.

For the first seven years of its modern history, the British Grand Prix was held exclusively at Silverstone, organised by the British Racing Drivers' Club, to whom the RAC delegated its authority. After that, the race venue alternated between Silverstone and Aintree, the circuit built round the famous Grand National horse-racing course on the outskirts of Liverpool, where the organisation was delegated to another national club, the British Automobile Racing Club. In 1964, the race went to the South of England for the first time, to Brands Hatch in Kent. This race, and all subsequent ones, was and have been organised by the RAC itself. Since then, the race has alternated between Silverstone and Brands Hatch.

The 1948 Grand Prix, at Silverstone, was a makeshift event for almost entirely pre-war cars, on what was still no more than a converted airfield. The 3¾-mile course was the perimeter track (as is the current circuit) plus lengthy sections of infield runway with straw-bale chicanes. The Maserati 4CLT was the car to beat, Luigi Villoresi winning in one in 1948 and Baron E. de Graffenried being similarly equipped in 1949.

It was not until 1950, the year of introduction of the World Championship, that the race reflected the growing stature of Grand Prix racing, with the all-conquering 158/9 Alfa Romeo (the legendary 'Alfetta') team showing how it should be done. The presence of their Majesties, King George VI and Queen Elizabeth, gave motor racing unprecedented respectability in British eyes, resulting in a crowd so vast (reported rather optimistically at the time as 100,000) that the traffic system failed completely.

Guiseppe Farina won (he took that first championship, too) from Luigi Fagioli with Reg Parnell, the British guest driver, completing the Alfa 1-2-3.

In 1951, it was the British Grand Prix which sounded the death knell of the 1½-litre supercharged) 4½-litre unsupercharged formula. Juan Manuel Fangio was to win the championship for Alfa Romeo, but Froilan Gonzales ('The Pampas Bull') won this race conclusively in the big Ferrari 4½-litre, with Fangio second. The writing was on the wall for Alfa Romeo, who withdrew from Formula One at the end of the season. Without them, the formula had no challenge for the new-found Ferrari dominance and, for the next two seasons, the World Championship was for Formula Two cars of 2 litres.

Alberto Ascari won the championship and the British Grand Prix for Ferrari, in both these years. In 1952, Piero Taruffi's Ferrari was second, but Mike Hawthorn was a courageous third in the hopelessly outpaced Cooper-Bristol. His driving earned him a regular seat with Ferrari the next season.

Formula One was revised for 1954–60 with cars allowed engines of up to 2½ litres unsupercharged and although there were no serious contenders, up to 750cc supercharged. It heralded a great new era of Grand Prix racing. The 1954 Silverstone race saw four-cylinder Ferraris first and second (Gonzales and Hawthorn) from Onofre Marimon's six-cylinder Maserati 250F, with Fangio a lowly fourth in the ill-handling eight-cylinder Mercedes-Benz W196,

with all-enveloping streamlined bodywork.

There was not much wrong with the handling of the open-wheeled W196 a year later when the post-war British Grand Prix was held for the first time on a circuit other than Silverstone. At Aintree, the Mercedes-Benz team augmented its usual three cars for Taruffi to take fourth place behind Stirling Moss, Fangio and Karl Kling. Moss made history that day as the first British driver ever to win the British Grand Prix.

Aintree was not universally popular as a Grand Prix circuit. The 3-mile circuit had been designed by a highways engineer and racing drivers disliked his constant radius bends. The paddock arrangements at that period were cramped and weather conditions of extreme heat coincided with a slight wind blowing odious fumes from an adjacent rayon factory over the public enclosures. However, it was a great and colourful occasion with a vast crowd, although, as at Silverstone five years previously, the 100,000 claimed was probably a substantial exaggeration.

With Ferraris and Maseratis outpaced by the Mercedes cars, the British effort seemed especially futile, but at least there were Vanwalls, Connaughts and, prophetically, a rear-engined Cooper, as well as a Bristol-engined converted sports car, privately entered by one Jack Brabham.

A year later, at Silverstone, with Mercedes having withdrawn from the scene, it was Ferrari versus Maserati again with Moss's Maserati taking fastest lap before retiring and Fangio winning for Ferrari. The only British finisher from a substantial contingent was Jack Fairman's Syracuse Connaught in fourth place, but Hawthorn and Tony Brooks had led splendidly in the new BRMs before succumbing to engine and chassis failures.

Aintree, in 1957, opened a new era of Grand Prix racing. It was one of the most tense British Grand Prix races in the entire history. Moss in the Vanwall led (not for the first time) only to stop, this time with persistent misfiring. He took over the car of Brooks, who was unfit through burns received in a Le Mans crash. Resuming in third place, Moss set a tremendous pace and looked capable of catching Jean Behra's Maserati and Hawthorn's Ferrari in the final laps. Then Behra's clutch exploded, Hawthorn's rear tyre punctured on some of the bits and Moss swept through to win the first Grande Epreuve with a British car for over 30 years (the Syracuse Grand Prix, which Brooks won in a Connaught in 1955 was a non-championship race). Almost as noteworthy were the fifth and sixth places, in rear-engined Coopers, of Roy Salvadori and Bob Gerard.

Salvadori, in a 2.2-litre Cooper-Climax, was third at Silverstone a year later behind Peter Collins and Hawthorn in Ferraris. It was to be the last British Grand Prix won by a front-engined car.

The next two years, at Aintree and Silverstone, saw Jack Brabham in 2½-litre Cooper-Climax cars, winning the British Grands Prix and the world championships, opening a period of almost complete domination by British constructors and British or Commonwealth drivers.

This near-stranglehold on Formula One led British teams to complacency. They demanded the continuation of the 2½-litre formula beyond 1960 and did little to prepare for the 1½-litre formula. The FIA declined to revise the change so that, at Aintree in 1961, there was that season's customary Ferrari walkover with Wolfgang Von Trips, Phil Hill (it was his championship year) and Richie Ginther 1-2-3 for the Italian constructor. It was to be eight years before a non-

*Above:* Pedro Rodriguez, BRM, leads a cortège of cars around Westfield bend at Brands Hatch in 1968's event. Following are Richard Attwood, Jacky Ickx, Jochen Rindt and Denny Hulme

*Centre:* a contrast in styles. Jochen Rindt, in the Lotus 49C, ahead of Jackie Stewart, Matra-Ford, at Silverstone in 1969. After 58 laps of close racing, Jochen had to stop at the pits to have an end plate, that was rubbing on a tyre, removed from his rear wing (see picture)

*Bottom left:* Jochen Rindt heads Jack Brabham at Brands Hatch in 1970. Rindt won, after Brabham ran out of fuel on the last lap

*Bottom right:* Emerson Fittipaldi, in the Lotus 72, overhauls Howden Ganley's BRM as they enter Stowe corner at Silverstone in 1971. Jackie Oliver, in a McLaren, follows

### British Grand Prix—results

1948—Silverstone: L. Villoresi (Maserati), 3 h 18 m 3 s, 72.38 mph.

1949—Silverstone: E. de Graffenreid (Maserati), 3 h 52 m 50.2 s, 77.31 mph.

1950—Silverstone: G. Farina (Alfa Romeo), 2 h 13 m 23.6 s, 90.95 mph.

1951—Silverstone: F. Gonzales (Ferrari), 2 h 42 m 18.2 s, 96.11 mph.

1952—Silverstone: A. Ascari (Ferrari), 2 h 44 m 11 s, 90.92 mph.

1953—Silverstone: A. Ascari (Ferrari), 2 h 50 m, 92.97 mph.

1954—Silverstone: F. Gonzales (Ferrari), 2 h 56 m 14 s, 89.69 mph.

1955—Aintree: S. Moss (Mercedes-Benz), 3 hr 7 m 21.2 s, 86.47 mph.

1956—Silverstone: J. M. Fangio (Ferrari), 2 h 59 m 47 s, 98.65 mph.

1957—Aintree: C. A. S. Brooks/S. Moss (Vanwall), 3 h 6 m 37.8 s, 86.80 mph.

1958—Silverstone: P. Collins (Ferrari), 2 h 9 m 4.2 s, 102.05 mph.

1959—Aintree: J. Brabham (Cooper-Climax), 2 h 30 m 11.6 s, 89.88 mph.

1960—Silverstone: J. Brabham (Cooper-Climax), 2 h 4 m 24.6 s, 108.69 mph.

1961—Aintree: W. Von Trips (Ferrari), 2 h 40 m 53.6 s, 83.91 mph.

1962—Aintree: J. Clark (Lotus-Climax), 2 h 26 m 20.8 s, 92.25 mph.

1963—Silverstone: J. Clark (Lotus-Climax), 2 h 14 m 9.6 s, 107.75 mph.

1964—Brands Hatch: J. Clark (Lotus-Climax), 2 h 15 m 7.0 s, 94.14 mph.

1965—Silverstone: J. Clark (Lotus-Climax), 2 h 5 m 25.4 s, 112.02 mph.

1966—Brands Hatch: J. Brabham (Brabham Repco), 2 h 13 m 13.4 s, 95.48 mph.

1967—Silverstone: J. Clark (Lotus Ford), 1 h 59 m 25.6 s, 117.64 mph.

1968—Brands Hatch: J. Siffert (Lotus Ford), 2 h 1 m 20.3 s, 104.83 mph.

1969—Silverstone: J. Stewart (Matra Ford), 1 h 55 m 55.6 s, 127.25 mph.

1970—Brands Hatch: J. Rindt (Lotus Ford), 1 h 57 m 2.0 s, 108.69 mph.

1971—Silverstone: J. Stewart (Tyrrell Ford), 1 h 31 m 31.5 s, 130.48 mph.

1972—Brands Hatch: E. Fittipaldi (Lotus Ford–John Player Special), 1 h 47 m 50.2 s, 112.06 mph.

1973—Silverstone: P. Revson (McLaren-Ford), 1 h 29 m 18.5 s, 131.75 mph.

British car (the French Matra) won the British Grand Prix again.

The next year's event was again held at Aintree, in honour of the organising BARC's Golden Jubilee. It was the last time successive British Grands Prix were held on the same circuit. By now Coventry-Climax had produced a new V8 as had BRM. Once more, British cars were in complete command and the finishing order was Jim Clark (Lotus-Climax), John Surtees (Lola-Climax), Bruce McLaren (Cooper-Climax) and Graham Hill (BRM).

For the rest of the 1½-litre Formula, Clark was the man to beat and, at the British Grand Prix, nobody managed to do so. At Silverstone in 1963, he led home Surtees (Ferrari) and Hill (BRM). At Brands Hatch in 1964, he was hounded all the way by Hill with Surtees third. At Silverstone in 1965, the first three were the same again.

Brands Hatch provided a very different challenge from either Silverstone or Aintree, being a sort of miniature Nürburgring, not only because of its undulations and varied corners but as a result of its bumps, demanding much more of suspensions and driving skills.

In 1965, at Silverstone, Clark's consummate skill was well demonstrated when he just held off Hill's BRM despite driving the last few laps coasting round corners to save his oil-starved engine.

Next year at Brands Hatch, the race was heralded as 'The Return of Power' as it was the first season of the current 3-litre Formula. In fact, one of the least powerful cars won: Jack Brabham, in his own Repco-powered car, with good reliability and fine handling, triumphed as the first man to win a Grand Prix in a car of his own construction. His own number two, Denny Hulme, was second.

In 1967, the Ford DFV engine was ready and began its period of overwhelming supremacy. Clark, in the Lotus 49, ran away with the Silverstone race from Hulme's Brabham and Chris Amon's Ferrari. A year later at Brands Hatch, the same type of car won, but it looked very different as the 'wings' era had begun and aerodynamic aids were at their most exotic. Graham Hill and Jackie Oliver in Gold Leaf Team Lotus cars both retired after leading, but Jo Siffert in Rob Walker's 49 kept ahead of Amon's Ferrari to win.

By then, Clark had died in a Formula Two crash at Hockenheim, but a new Scots star was rising and Jackie Stewart put the Matra in front at Silverstone in the first of his Championship years, with Jackie Ickx (Brabham) and Bruce McLaren in his own car, second and third respectively.

In 1970, Jochen Rindt was in the new Lotus 72 to give the car a lucky win after Brabham, who had been in complete command, ran out of fuel on the very last lap of a most exciting Brands Hatch race. Hulme was third for McLaren, by a car's length, from Clay Regazzoni's Ferrari.

The 1971 race was called the Woolmark British Grand Prix and marked the first full-scale sponsorship of the British classic. Stewart, always much happier at Silverstone than at Brands Hatch, won comfortably in the Tyrrell which was to give him his second World Championship. Ronnie Peterson beat off plenty of strong opposition to be second in a March.

The word 'British' disappeared in 1972 when the race became the John Player Grand Prix. Emerson Fittipaldi, who had begun his European racing, in Formula Ford and Formula Three, at Brands Hatch only three years previously, gave the race sponsors a tremendous boost by taking the John Player Special (née Lotus 72) to victory from Stewart's Tyrrell and Peter Revson's Yardley McLaren.

The enormous advances in both racing-car safety construction and circuit safety were demonstrated effectively at Silverstone during 1973, which heralded the British Grand Prix's worst-ever crash. At the end of the first lap, Jody Scheckter's McLaren spun in the middle of the pack and an enormous multiple pile-up followed, causing the race to be stopped. Miraculously, only Andrea de Adamich was injured, breaking a leg in his crushed Brabham. The re-run race was won by Revson's McLaren—his first GP win—from Peterson's John Player Special and Denny Hulme in another McLaren.

If a spectator, able to watch only one Grand Prix a year, wished to choose that which would give him the best chance of assessing the season's World Championship contenders, he could scarcely choose better than the British Grand Prix. More often than not, the winner also takes the Championship. Indeed, since the Championship began, it has been a three-to-one chance that the winner of the title will come either first or second in the British Grand Prix of that year. GM

*Below left:* Rolf Stommelen, Eifelland-Ford, leads Dave Charlton, Lucky-Strike Lotus, Chris Amon, Matra-Simca and Nicki Lauda, works March around South bank at Brands in '72

*Below right:* after a disastrous crash at the start of the '73 GP at Silverstone, racing soon got under way again. Here, Clay Regazzoni, BRM, leads James Hunt, Hesketh-March and Howden Ganley, ISO-Marlboro, through Woodcote. Note that Hunt's car has Mike Beuttler's airbox fitted, after Hunt's own was knocked off in the first lap crash, and Beuttler himself had to retire

This magnificent four-color encyclopedia is brought to you by Columbia House
in cooperation with Orbis Publishing Ltd., one of Great Britain's most enterprising publishers.
Rather than change any of the encyclopedia's authoritative international automotive text, we have
included a glossary of terms that will give you immediate American equivalents, a conversion table
for the international metric system, and a conversion table for equivalent monetary values.

# Glossary

| BRITISH | AMERICAN | BRITISH | AMERICAN |
|---|---|---|---|
| Aerial | Antenna | Motor | Engine |
| Aluminium | Aluminum | Number plate | License plate |
| Apron | Skirt | Overrider | Bumper guard |
| Big-end | Rod (conrod) bearing | Paraffin | Kerosene |
| Blower (colloquial) | Supercharger | Parking brake | Parking lock |
| Bonnet | Hood | Petrol | Gasoline, "gas" |
| Boot | Trunk | Petrol pump | Gasoline or fuel pump |
| Brake servo | Power brake | Production car | Stock car |
| Bulkhead | Firewall | Propellor shaft | Drive shaft |
| Capacity | Displacement | Quarter light | Door vent |
| Carburetter; carburettor | Carburetor | | |
| Check strap | Door stop | Rear lamp | Tail light |
| Clutch release bearing | Clutch throwout bearing | Rear seat squab | Rear setback or backrest |
| Control box | Voltage regulator | Reverse lamp | Back up light |
| Crown wheel and pinion | Ring gear and pinion | Roof lamp | Dome light |
| Cylinder block | Cylinder crankcase | Saloon | Sedan |
| Dip switch | Dimmer switch | Scuttle | Cowl |
| Door pillar | Door post | Selector rod | Shift bar |
| Drop arm | Pitman arm | Servo-assisted | Power-assisted |
| Drop-head | Convertible | Side lamp | Parking light |
| Dynamo | Generator | Side member | Side rail |
| Epicylic gearbox | Planetary gearbox | Spanner | Wrench |
| Exhaust silencer | Muffler | Sparking plug | Spark plug |
| Facia panel | Dashboard | Starting handle | Crank handle |
| | | Steering column | Steering post |
| Gear lever | Gear shift lever | Steering relay | Steering idler |
| Gearbox | Transmission | Stub axle | Steering knuckle |
| Gearbox housing | Transmission casing | Sump | Pan |
| Gearchange | Gearshift | Swivel pin | King pin |
| Glassfibre | Fiberglass | Toe board | Toe pan |
| Grease nipple | Grease fitting | Track | Tread |
| Gudgeon pin | Piston or wrist pin | Track rod | Tie bar or track bar |
| Half shaft | Axle shaft | Two-stroke | Two-cycle |
| Handbrake | Parking brake | Tyre | Tire |
| Hose clip | Hose clamp | Valance | Rocker panel |
| Ignition harness | Ignition set | Wheel arch | Wheelhouse or housing |
| Kerb | Curb | Wheel brace | Wheel wrench |
| Layshaft | Counter shaft | Windscreen | Windshield |
| | | Wing | Fender |
| Main shaft | Output shaft | Wishbone | A-arm; Control arm |
| Marque | Brand, make | Works | Plant, factory |

# Metric Equivalents

## Length

| | | | |
|---|---|---|---|
| Centimeter (Cm.) | = 0.3937 in. | In. | = 2.5400 cm. |
| Meter (M.) | = 3.2808 ft. | Ft. | = 0.3048 m. |
| Meter | = 1.0936 yd. | Yd. | = 0.9144 m. |
| Kilometer (Km.) | = 0.6214 mile | Mile | = 1.6093 km. |

## Area

| | | | |
|---|---|---|---|
| Sq. cm. | = 0.1550 sq. in. | Sq. in. | = 6.4516 sq. cm. |
| Sq. m. | = 10.7639 sq. ft. | Sq. ft. | = 0.0929 sq. m. |
| Sq. m. | = 1.1960 sq. yd. | Sq. yd. | = 0.8361 sq. m. |
| Hectare | = 2.4710 acres | Acre | = 0.4047 hectar |
| Sq. km. | = 0.3861 sq. mile | Sq. mile | = 2.5900 sq. km. |

## Volume

| | | | |
|---|---|---|---|
| Cu. cm. | = 0.0610 cu. in. | Cu. in. | = 16.3872 cu. cm. |
| Cu. m. | = 35.3145 cu. ft. | Cu. ft. | = 0.0283 cu. m. |
| Cu. m. | = 1.3079 cu. yd. | Cu. yd. | = 0.7646 cu. m. |

## Capacity

| | | | |
|---|---|---|---|
| Liter | = 61.0250 cu. in. | Cu. in. | = 0.0164 liter |
| Liter | = 0.0353 cu. ft. | Cu. ft. | = 28.3162 liters |
| Liter | = 0.2642 gal. (U.S.) | Gal. | = 3.7853 liters |
| Liter | = 0.0284 bu. (U.S.) | Bu. | = 35.2383 liters |

Liter = $\begin{cases} 1000.027 \text{ cu. cm.} \\ 1.0567 \text{ qt. (liquid) or } 0.9081 \text{ qt. (dry)} \\ 2.2046 \text{ lb. of pure water at 4 C} = 1 \text{ kg.} \end{cases}$

## Weight

| | | | |
|---|---|---|---|
| Gram. (Gm.) | = 15.4324 grains | Grain | = 0.0648 gm. |
| Gram | = 0.0353 oz. | Oz. | = 28.3495 gm. |
| Kilogram (Kg.) | = 2.2046 lb. | Lb. | = 0.4536 kg. |
| Kg. | = 0.0011 ton (sht.) | Ton (sht.) | = 907.1848 kg. |
| Ton (met.) | = 1.1023 ton (sht.) | Ton (sht.) | = 0.9072 ton (met.) |
| Ton (met.) | = 0.9842 ton (lg.) | Ton (lg.) | = 1.0160 ton (met.) |

## Pressure

| | |
|---|---|
| 1 kg. per sq. cm. | = 14.223 lb. per sq. in. |
| 1 lb. per sq. in. | = 0.0703 kg. per sq. cm. |
| 1 kg. per sq. m. | = 0.2048 lb. per sq. ft. |
| 1 lb. per sq. ft. | = 4.8824 kg. per sq. m. |
| 1 kg. per sq. cm. | = 0.9678 normal atmosphere |

1 normal atmosphere = $\begin{cases} 1.0332 \text{ kg. per sq. cm.} \\ 1.0133 \text{ bars} \\ 14.696 \text{ lb. per sq. in.} \end{cases}$

# Approximate Values of the Pound (£)

| | |
|---|---|
| 1914-1919 | $4.76 |
| 1935 | 4.90 |
| 1936 | 4.97 |
| 1937 | 4.94 |
| 1938 | 4.89 |
| 1939 | 4.46 |
| 1940-1949 | 4.03 |
| 1950-1967 | 2.80 |
| 1968-1970 | 2.40 |
| 1971-1972 | $2.40/2.60 |
| 1972-Present | 2.60/2.10 |